MW00633157

Treasures from Heaven

Recollections of a Pediatric Nurse

Also by S. F. Johnson

Seasons at Rose Cottage

The Landlady's Handbook

Cancer and Me

Little Hen's Big Adventure

A Child's ABC's of Gardening

Grandpa's on the Potty

Samuel Kitty Finds a Home

Treasures from Heaven

Recollections of a Pediatric Nurse

S. F. Johnson

ISBN: 978-0-9600773-7-3

Cover design by the Author

Names have been changed or abbreviated to protect the individual's privacy.

Author's Note

I earned my Associate Degree in nursing while I was married, with children. The nursing program was a two-year program, and I became pregnant with my third child during the first year, and gave birth on the Friday before my second year of nursing school was to begin three days later.

Needless to say, I decided to sit out a year with my darling new baby girl, and finish my degree the following year. Growing up, I had always wanted to be a veterinarian, and had even obtained my Bachelor of Science degree in Zoology from the University of California, Davis. After graduating, I had applied to veterinarian school there once, and had received a rejection letter.

After meeting and marrying my husband, I decided that instead, I would become a pediatric nurse. Thus, began my journey to becoming a nurse.

After graduating from nursing school, my main focus remained on raising my children, so I worked part-time as a medical-surgical nurse every weekend at a local children's hospital, while my husband could care for our children.

A few years later, I switched from working every weekend to working every Wednesday evening, and every other weekend. I loved my job, and all of the children I cared for along the way. Hospital nursing can be a difficult, stressful job, but very rewarding. A good nurse can make a real difference in their patient's outcomes during their hospitalization.

Sixteen years later, after being diagnosed and treated for breast cancer, I left the med-surg floor and after a residency, started working in the operating room. Here, are a few of my recollections from my nursing career.

Children are an heritage from the Lord - Psalms 127:3

Children truly are 'Treasures from Heaven.'

Chapter

1

My nursing instructor must have been more than frustrated at the caliber of student she was forced to work with, in me. We both stood in front of a patient that had a hard fiberglass cast on her left leg. My instructor asked me what my main concern should be regarding this patient, and I hadn't a clue! I was so inexperienced and green, that I was still just trying to remember where I had placed my sack lunch for the day!

The answer of course, was that I should have been concerned that the cast had the potential of being too tight, which could cut off the blood supply or damage nerves to that leg. That is why your nurse is frequently checking your toes if the cast is on your leg; or your fingers, if you have a cast on your arm. Your toes or fingers, should remain pink and warm, indicating that they are receiving adequate circulation. Casts that have become too constricting also can cause pain for the patient, so that is also a concern the nurse should be aware of. If there is pain or poor blood flow to the extremities, and the problem is caught early, the cast can be cut or bivalved, thus relieving the pressure, preventing any permanent damage.

Later, after I became a nurse and worked on the medical-surgical ward, I was involved several times with calling the surgeon, and having the surgeon come to bivalve a cast. A cast saw was used to cut down both sides of the hard cast, which immediately eliminated any constriction to the affected limb. Then, a bandage was used to wrap the two pieces of the cast together, so that it remained on the limb. Amazingly, cast saws have special blades that are designed to cut the hard surface of the cast, but not the skin underneath it!

Nursing school was a combination of in-class education,

along with hands-on experience we gained at various hospitals and nursing homes that were gracious enough to let a bunch of nursing students descend on their facilities.

As students, we were taught how to take the vital signs of our patients. Listening to the heart with a stethoscope was fairly simple, if you were just counting the heart beating. Listening for a heart murmur was way out of league for us at that time as students. Counting respirations with a stethoscope, or by simply looking at the chest rise and fall was also quite easy. Later, listening to actual lung sounds such as wheezing or rhonchi, was a more advanced skill.

The one skill that I found the most difficult and frustrating as a student, was obtaining a blood pressure with a stethoscope and sphygmomanometer. Just the name of the blood pressure device should have clued me in to the fact that this was to be no easy feat to achieve! To start, an inflatable sphygmomanometer cuff is placed around the upper part of the person's arm. A bulb is attached by a rubber tube to the cuff, and a small blood pressure gauge is also attached to the cuff by another rubber tube.

Somehow, you are expected to squeeze the bulb repeatedly to inflate the cuff, hold the gauge up so that you can read it, all the while placing your stethoscope firmly over the brachial artery of the patient's arm! Oh, and I forgot to mention that the bulb has a little screw that you turn to keep the cuff inflated, or to release the pressure in the cuff! How a person with only two hands was expected to do all this was beyond me!

The whole idea is to inflate the cuff tightly until the person's systolic blood pressure is stopped from passing below the cuff, where your stethoscope is placed on the arm. Systolic pressure is the maximum pressure your heart puts out when it is contracting. Diastolic on the other hand, is the lower pressure in your arteries when your heart is not contracting.

After pumping up the cuff to 180mm Hg or higher, you are supposed to slowly release air from the cuff by turning the little screw, all the while listening intently with your stethoscope placed over the arm, and holding up the gauge so that you can read it! You are listening for the first loud sounds of blood as it flows internally under your stethoscope, which is the systolic pressure, followed by the quiet muffling of the sound along with the sound stopping, which is the diastolic pressure; memorizing the two blood pressure numbers as you watch the needle on the gauge go down.

After practicing in the classroom setting, we as student nurses, were then assigned real patients at the hospital. One day, I was assigned to an elderly woman to take her vital signs, including her blood pressure. I placed the cuff on the woman's arm, and with my stethoscope in place while trying to manage holding the gauge; I began pumping up the cuff. I began releasing the air from the cuff, only to hear absolutely nothing! Beads of sweat began to break out on my forehead, as I apologized to my patient, and asked if I could try again. She was more than amicable, as she had nothing else happening on her social calendar at that moment, plus most patients were more than accommodating with helping student nurses.

After several tries with still hearing absolutely no sound of any kind, and wondering about my choice of career, I meekly explained my predicament to my instructor. My instructor reviewed the patient's history. The patient was there in the hospital to have her lower limbs amputated because of poor perfusion! Her general poor perfusion was also the reason why I, nor anyone else, could obtain a blood pressure reading. She probably was not the ideal patient to have been assigned to a student nurse.

Besides learning to take vital signs, we as students, were taught how to give bed baths, and to give injections. Administering IM, or intramuscular injections was another area that gave me inordinate stress. After practicing on inserting IM injections into an orange, giving the actual injection was no big deal, as long as you were dealing with an orange! The clincher was that if you happened to give an IM injection in the wrong area of the patient's body and hit a nerve instead of muscle, you could cause nerve damage! We studied anatomy, and memorized all of the major nerves to stay clear of when injecting a patient. Another thing that was taught to us, was that you should always draw back on the syringe just before injecting the medicine, to make sure that you hadn't inadvertently hit a blood vessel, which could be potentially bad; since you would then be giving the medicine IV, or intravenous, instead of IM. I can only remember one time in my entire nursing career giving an IM injection where I drew back, and blood entered my syringe. I cannot tell you the level of surprise I felt when that happened, as it was so rare!

During class, as we listened to hours of lectures from our instructor, a fellow nursing student and I loved to visit quietly with each other. We had previously learned the importance of washing our hands; in fact, it had been drilled into us over and over, how important the act of washing our hands was. Thinking to embarrass us as we visited, our instructor during her lecture would suddenly ask my friend or myself what the answer to her question was. Of course, neither of us even knew what the question was, as we had not been paying attention. Our answer always was, "Good hand washing is the most important practice." What could the instructor say?

Both of us graduated, and my friend went on to work in the pediatric intensive care unit for many years before becoming part of the administration at the same children's hospital, and I have continued working part-time for over thirty-five years. Just goes to show you there is hope, even for smart-alecks!

For homework in nursing school, we wrote countless nursing care plans, writing about what disease our patient had, and what our plan of action to help them would be.

When I became pregnant during the second half of my first year of nursing school, I did not feel well at all. Nauseated and extremely tired, one of the patients I had been assigned to care for in the hospital one day was a very elderly man. Oh, how I longed to just lie down for a moment or two on the hospital bed he happened to be in! I wondered who should be taking care of whom, since I felt particularly bad that day. I also knew that it would be the end of my short-lived career in nursing if I were to be found lying next to my patient! Not to mention the surprise the very elderly gentleman would have had finding a pregnant student nurse lying next to him!

While I was a student nurse, one of my patients was a young working nurse. She had come into the hospital because the pupil in her left eye was completely dilated, which was a sign of suffering a cerebral stroke. She was very upset, and the young nurse called her mother to let her know that she had been hospitalized for a possible stroke. Her mother discounted the whole idea that her young, healthy daughter had suffered a stroke, and told her daughter that it had to somehow be work-related, and that she was sure her daughter was fine. It turned out that the mother was completely right! After several tests were done, it was determined that while at work that morning, the young nurse had accidentally been sprayed in that eye with some medication which had dilated her pupil!

My stint as a student nurse meant that I had a brief rotation in the operating room. There in the OR, I was allowed to scrub in, and hold a retractor on my patient, who was having her gall bladder removed. As the surgeon began the operation, and the knife blade first cut into her skin on her abdomen, I was amazed at how yellow human fat was! I also remember being surprised at what a thick layer of fat she had, as she was a fairly slim person. It didn't take long before I could hear ringing in my ears, and I knew that in a few moments I would pass out! I spoke up, and was quickly excused, and told to go to the lounge, sit down, and put my head between my legs! I wonder now, if the staff in the OR had taken bets to see how long I would last!

Another time in nursing school, I spent the day watching a gastroenterologist scoping different patients to assess them for various problems. The male gastroenterologist happened to be very good-looking. A sweet, very proper, older lady was one of his first patients. After the surgeon administered drugs to partially sedate her, the first words out of her mouth were, "doctor, you are SO good-looking!" My thoughts exactly! However, I knew that she would have died a thousand deaths if she knew that she had said it! The surgeon smiled slightly over her comment. He probably heard it routinely several times a day!

As part of our nursing education, we had to spend some time in a psychiatric facility. All of us were fairly apprehensive about this, as people afflicted with mental illness do not always behave in a rational manner.

The facility I was assigned to was a very old facility. It had a large campus, and the psychiatric ward was a locked one. On the same campus, was another area housing convicted sexual predators! At this same facility, a psychiatric patient had recently murdered another patient! Our instructor informed us that she thought that as students we would not be harmed, as that would be considered very bad even among the inmates! We were not totally convinced! You can only imagine our delight at this assignment.

My patient was an older woman whose main delusion was that she thought both of her feet were lobsters, and she was always suggesting that we get some butter and eat them!

The locked psych-ward was located up on the second story of the old brick building, and a long staircase had to be climbed before you arrived at the locked door. Each student was given a key to unlock the door. Inside, were several offices for administration, along with a very large room that served as a family room of sorts for the patients. In the large family room was a pool-table, couches and chairs. A large TV was mounted high up on one wall. One patient I observed was playing pool, but when a commercial showing Michael Jackson singing and dancing would come on, the patient would immediately become Michael Jackson as well, and start singing and dancing. It seemed common for mentally-ill people to take on the delusion that they were a famous person in our society, like Michael Jackson.

In a corner of the family room was a window where medications were dispensed to the various patients. In another area of the facility were locked isolation rooms. I was allowed to take my patient outside for walks, which is what I usually did.

On our walks, we would sometimes see some of the sexual predators walking together, always in pairs for some reason. They were allowed to roam the campus freely, which I thought was strange, as they could have just roamed off the unfenced campus back into civilization.

I was always nervous and wary, as my patient and I came near to any pairs of sexual predators on our walks. I knew my patient would be absolutely no help at all to me if I was attacked, but fortunately that never happened. We were taught in class that if our patients wanted to talk about their delusions, we were to say, "I don't want to talk about it." It was felt that to help the patient, we didn't want to encourage them in their delusion. Even denying their delusions to them was seen as reinforcing. I also found the simple statement "I don't want to talk about it," quite helpful in my normal day to day living! It gave you permission to not discuss something that you didn't want to talk about at that moment. I thought it was interesting that my mentally challenged patient would honor my request to 'not talk about it.' She always quit talking about her delusion right away. Interesting!

Later, I encountered a staff member who did try and argue with my patient, telling her that her feet were not lobsters, all the while my patient kept insisting that her feet were indeed lobsters, and where was the butter!

At most hospitals, as student nurses, we were instructed on

how to handle emergencies. Who to call, how to call, etcetera. At the psychiatric facility, we were told that only the seasoned staff would be handling any emergencies. That was fine with me!

One day, my patient and I returned from our walk. After we had climbed the long staircase, and I had unlocked the door, we both entered inside and turned to walk down the hallway. There lying on the floor was a staff RN, and two orderlies struggling with an out of control patient, and it looked like the patient was winning! With horror in her eyes, the RN looked up at me and shouted for me to get help! I ran around trying to decide who to get, or how to call for help, as we had never even been given an emergency phone number! Finally, I was able to get help, and the patient was subdued, and put into an isolation room.

After I graduated from nursing school, there was a plethora of inexperienced nurses looking for work, and so I had a hard time getting anyone to hire me. This same psychiatric facility told me that they would love to have me come and work there. I politely declined.

It was frustrating for me not to be hired at the local children's hospital I wished to work at, because of my inexperience. Hospitals each have their own nurse recruiter that looks for, and hires staff. I asked the nurse recruiter; how can I get any experience if someone doesn't first hire me, so I can work and gain experience? She would always apologize, and tell me that when I had experience to reapply.

I finally decided to volunteer with the Red Cross at a local army base to try and get my foot in the door somewhere, so I could gain experience, and get hired. Not long after that, the same nurse recruiter that was over the children's hospital, as well as two other hospitals the same organization owned, started a support group for all of the many recent nursing graduates who couldn't get hired at that time!

Sign me up! What better way to get your foot in the door than to get to know the person who did all the hiring! Here was my chance for me to spend time with the very nurse recruiter that had the power to give me the job I wanted most! For our support group meetings, we all met in the hospital, and talked about how frustrating it was that we had gone to nursing school, and yet were unable to find jobs. This all sounds very funny now as I write this thirty-five years later, while there is a severe nursing shortage!

Long story, short; I, and one other nurse out of the group of about seven nurses attending the support group were hired by the nurse recruiter. I was given the job I wanted at the local children's hospital. Within only a couple of years after I had graduated from nursing school, hospitals were so short of nurses, that they were actively recruiting to hire even nursing school students as soon as they graduated!

Chapter

2

After graduating from nursing school, I had to wait a few months before I could take my state board exam. Decades ago, when I took the exam, it was offered only once or twice a year, and you had to take the exam in person. Can you imagine now, that computers didn't exist at all back then? To take the test, you went to a facility that had an enormous room filled with desks. You were searched before entering the room, and people were placed throughout the room, ensuring that no cheating could take place. The test, as I remember, lasted several hours. If you needed to use the restroom, one of the people there to ensure there was no cheating, accompanied you to the bathroom! After taking the exam, you had to wait for several days before you found out if you had passed or failed. Coupled with the fact that you could only take the test twice a year, meant that if you failed, you would have to wait six more months before being able to take it again, and you would be unable to have a job as a registered nurse until you passed.

A side note for those interested in nostalgia: when I graduated, you could obtain your registered nurse license one of three ways: one; you could get a bachelor of science degree in nursing. Two; you could get your associate's degree in nursing, or three; you could get a diploma in nursing from a hospital where they offered their own nursing program. All three candidates sat for, and took the same state board exam.

I obtained my associate's degree in nursing from a local community college. I had previously acquired a bachelor of science degree in Zoology from a University. Originally, I had wanted to become a veterinarian, but had decided after marrying, that nursing would fit into my life-style better.

After obtaining a job at the local children's hospital, I was placed under the tutelage of Janet, an experienced nurse who was and is, a very fun person with an acute sense of humor.

Not long after I had started to work at the pediatric hospital, we had a case where a little girl had come to us from the emergency room after ingesting a harmful substance. Usually, the patient is given activated charcoal to neutralize the harmful substance while still in the emergency room, but somehow this task fell to us. Both Janet and I thought this was a strange order as several hours had passed by, and obviously the child was doing well; and the likelihood of the charcoal being needed at this point was not too great. However, an order is an order, so we proceeded to fulfill it.

We took the child along with her mother to a treatment room. The treatment room was a small room off the main hallway on the med-surg floor of the hospital, and its walls were lined with pink tile for easy cleaning. Children, as well as adults, are not going to volunteer to drink a bunch of charcoal, so a nasogastric, or ng tube was placed by us. As one can imagine, not too many children are going to lie quietly during this procedure, which is why two nurses were needed: one, to hold the child, and the other to place the ng tube. This was done by measuring from the child's mouth to her ear and then down to below the xiphoid process on her chest. A small piece of tape was placed on the tube to mark the measurement of how far down to place the tube, once it was inserted. The tube was lubricated, the child's head was placed forward towards her chest a little, and then the tube was gently pushed down one side of her nose. A syringe filled with air was then attached to the end of the ng tube, and while Janet placed a stethoscope over the girl's stomach, Janet injected the air from the syringe, listening for a gurgling noise. Then, the plunger on the syringe was pulled back, with the expectation that stomach fluid should come back, which it did. This process assures the nurse that she has not inadvertently placed the ng in the lungs, which would have catastrophic results when injecting any kind of fluid.

The ng placement went smoothly. Next, we shook the charcoal mixture up, and placed it in a very large syringe that was then attached to the end of the nasogastric tube. Unfortunately, since neither of us were experienced in using charcoal, we didn't know that activated charcoal tends to have very large globs in it, and needs to be shaken for a VERY long time, which we didn't do.

As soon as we proceeded to push the charcoal down the ng tube, a blob of charcoal became lodged inside the tube and we could no longer get the charcoal to go down easily. We both knew that we did not want to go through placing another ng tube in this poor child, so Janet decided to give the charcoal-filled syringe the old heave-ho by pushing on the syringe plunger with all the muscle she had, and blam! The syringe came apart from the ng and charcoal sprayed everywhere, and I mean everywhere! When I looked up at Janet, her face was completely black, and only her eyes and teeth were white! Apparently, I also looked the same to her. Charcoal was all over the walls, and we both lost it! Professionalism went right out the window, as we started to laugh so hard that we were crying. The mother was the only appropriate person there, as she tried to console her unhappy child. Just then, the ward secretary knocked on the treatment room door, and peaked around the corner. Seeing the blackened disaster along with the two blackened nurses, she gave out a little gasp, but recovered quickly with "shall I call housekeeping?" At that point, we decided that we had carried out the doctor's orders far enough, and we were done. I am still amazed that we weren't written up for our inappropriate behavior that day!

As nurses, we never knew what situation might present itself to us. Our hospital was located centrally in a less desirable part of the city. It was not unusual for mentally-ill people to find their way up to the second floor of the hospital where the medical-surgical floor was. Many times, they would come up in pairs where one of these delusional visitors would be telling the other person how they were the doctor, and explaining all about the various patients they were caring for, which of course was not true. Security would be immediately alerted while we intervened, and the two visitors would be escorted out of the building by security. Another time, a single, older, mentally-ill woman was standing in front of the elevators, staring intently for an unusually long time. When I asked her if I could be of help to her, she stated that she wanted to go up to the seventh floor. The problem was the hospital only had three floors!

On the medical-surgical floor, we had three wings radiating out from a central nurse's station. One wing was only used when the volume of patients was very high. At this time, the extra wing remained empty.

We had recently admitted a very sad case involving a young teenage girl that was a near-drowning. Unfortunately, she was the worst-case scenario.... alive, but for all intents and purposes, non-functional. She would never talk, walk, eat or do any of those normal functions again. The girl and her family had recently immigrated from Viet Nam during a time when we had seen a large influx of refugees in our area. Her family came to see her every day, and her mother was quite pregnant. The girl had been at the hospital for several weeks, and was awaiting placement in a long-term care facility.

One day, her mother without telling anyone, went down to the far room of the empty unused wing, and decided it was time to give birth there alone! Somehow, someone found out what was about to happen, and alerted the medical residents. Residents are newly graduated medical doctors who learn various fields of medicine by spending time working in those different areas. One of the residents arrived in the mother's room just in time to deliver the newly arriving baby. The resident was beaming with pleasure as he recounted over and over to us how he had delivered the baby!

It took me about one year of working on the med-surg floor to develop my nursing judgement that would enable me to know which patients were stable, and which ones were not. It also enabled me to prioritize the many tasks that lay before me, as I started each shift.

During my sixteen years of working part-time on the medical-surgical floor, many nursing models were used. For a few years, an RN would have four patients which she would care for completely. This model was called 'primary care.' It included doing everything for your patient including taking vital signs, giving all of their medications, feeding them if they were babies, or too young to feed themselves, etc. Another model used, was one where the RN would have two LPN's (licensed practical nurses) working with her, with the registered nurse being in charge. Using this model, one time I was assigned to be in charge of thirteen patients! Now, keep in mind, that at our pediatric hospital, the only person allowed to give the medications was the RN, so I had thirteen patients that I was responsible for giving all their medications to, as well as overseeing their vital signs, physician's orders, and their general welfare. You rarely ever took your fifteen-minute morning or afternoon break, as you were so busy trying to keep up with the workload.

I was surprised when I first came out of nursing school and started working, to discover that the registered nurse plays a major role in their patient's recovery from illness. The nurse is there with the patient for at least eight hours at a stretch while their doctor checks in once a day, usually early in the morning. This means that it is up to the nurse to assess the patient's condition, and determine if what the doctor ordered is helping, or if the nurse needs to contact the doctor, and suggest a different course of action.

Medical doctors graduate from medical school in June, so every July we would have a group of brand new physicians hit the floor for their pediatric residency. This would be quite daunting to them, and they would rely heavily on the experienced nurses for advice on what to do in different situations.

One day, I had a respiratory patient on oxygen that just wasn't doing well. I had watched the young boy become progressively worse throughout the morning, and was concerned enough about him that I felt it was in his best interest to have him transferred to the pediatric intensive care unit or PICU, where he could be monitored more closely. One tool that is used extensively in the hospital is an oxygen saturation monitor. This monitor gives out a reading of the percentage of oxygen that is in the patient's bloodstream. It consists of a light embedded in a flexible bandage that wraps around the patient's finger, or in a non-disposable clip that goes over a finger. When I called one of the residents to get an order to move the patient to the PICU, one of the resident's first questions to me was what was the patient's oxygen saturation level? Now, it just so happened that the patient's oxygen saturation monitor was reading the saturation as being ninety-six percent, which is a good saturation level. The resident stated that the patient was doing fine, and refused to give me the order to move the patient to the PICU. I told the resident that I wanted an order for an arterial blood gas.

A blood gas gives you a genuine snapshot of how well the patient is doing. To obtain a blood gas, a respiratory therapist comes and draws a tiny amount of blood, which is taken to the lab and analyzed. The resident agreed to give me a phone order for the blood gas draw, and it was accomplished. A few minutes later, I got the blood gas results which were bad, and confirmed my assessment--that the patient wasn't doing well at all. With this news, multiple residents came running up to the patient's room to see him. The next thing I knew they had all left again.... but had forgotten to give me the order to move him to the PICU!!! I called them again on the telephone, and they sheepishly gave me the order to move him to the PICU. The patient was moved to the PICU where he could be watched more closely, as the patient to nurse ratio is much lower than on the med-surg floor, and the young boy made a complete recovery.

Sometimes, as I arrived on the med-surg floor to begin my shift, I would notice the crash cart next to a patient's room. The crash cart was a metal cart with several drawers which held drugs and other equipment needed in emergencies. The cart was on wheels, and could be moved easily, and the cart was usually located in an alcove along the wall of the med-surg floor. Having the crash cart next to a patient's room always got my attention right away, as I felt that any patient that needed to have the crash cart next to their room belonged in the pediatric intensive care unit, so they could be watched more closely. Usually, the PICU nurse only had one or two patients to look after, while the RN and two LPNs on the med-surg floor might be responsible for up to thirteen patients!

The most common reason that the crash cart was used was to give Narcan to a patient that was becoming unresponsive due to their receiving an opioid pain medication. Opioids were routinely given to post-surgical patients, as well as to patients in traction for broken legs, and the medication could lead to respiratory depression. Patients on opioids needed to be monitored closely, and always had EKG leads as well as oxygen saturation monitors in place that would alarm if not within normal limits. Giving Narcan would quickly reverse the effects of the opioid. The only problem with Narcan was that it had a very short half-life, meaning its effect would wear off quickly, and the patient could become unresponsive again, so close monitoring was necessary, and a second dose of Narcan might be required.

As I began my shift, if the patient with the crash cart next to their room was assigned to me, my first priority was to assess the patient's condition, and to get them moved to the PICU if I thought their condition warranted it.

On the other hand, it was not uncommon for infants and children to be undermedicated after having had surgery. Infants tend to sleep when they are in pain, so they appear as if they are comfortable. I remember one of my patients that was a post-surgical infant, that had not received any pain medication for a lengthy period of time, but was asleep. I began giving the infant the correct dosage of opioid medication during my shift. The baby awoke and began to eat vigorously, and kick its legs. As my shift wore on, and I gave a second dose of medication, the infant began to appear to be a little 'snowed' to me. It was also common for very young infants to have a liver that was not quite working as well as it should yet. The liver metabolizes drugs, converting active drugs to an inactive form. In my verbal report to the oncoming nurse, I warned her that she should probably hold off for a while on giving the infant any more opioid medication. The infant went on to do well during its stay at the hospital.

I was always proud of myself that during my sixteen years of working on the med-surg floor, I never had a child code. I think this was due partly to the fact that I aggressively advocated for them to be moved to the PICU if I felt they were unstable.

As nurses, we had just been given a course on communication. In the class, we had been taught that something like eighty-percent of communication was body language, while only twenty-percent of what is communicated was verbal. I personally had a hard time believing that body language was given so much emphasis when it came to communicating with a parent, or other family members. I also prided myself in having fairly good communication skills, especially if someone was upset. Sometimes, besides being a 'floor,' or med-surg nurse, I would work as the supervisor for the entire med-surg department.

One night while working as the supervisor, I was called and told that a mother was very upset, and was getting ready to take her child and leave AMA. AMA stands for 'against medical advice.' It is my understanding that if you have private health insurance and leave AMA, your hospital bill will not be paid for by your insurance company, and you will have to pay for it on your own.

Besides that, it is never good for the patient's health to leave AMA, so I went down to the room where the mother and child were staying. I decided to put my newly acquired knowledge to the test, and after entering the room and introducing myself, I sat down and didn't say a word. The mother ranted and raved about the poor care her child was receiving, and how no one was listening to her. She carried on for a few minutes and then, like magic, she was done. She decided that she, and her child, would stay in the hospital, and not leave AMA. I hadn't said a word! After that, I was a total believer in body language.

It was not uncommon to have an infant or two on the med-surg floor being treated for jaundice caused by hyperbilirubinemia, which means an excess of bilirubin. Bilirubin is produced by the normal breakdown of spent red blood cells, and low levels of bilirubin are found in everyone's blood. In these cases, the jaundice was caused by the new baby's liver being slow to start removing the bilirubin that was being released as some of the infant's red blood cells broke down. Bilirubin levels usually peak between the third and seventh day from the baby's birth.

Symptoms included a yellow hue to the baby's skin, as well as in the whites of their eyes. Left untreated, the high levels of bilirubin could cause mental retardation. To treat their elevated bilirubin levels, the infant, clad only in a diaper, would be placed inside an isolette, which had several long bili-lights mounted inside the top of the isolette. The baby's eyes were covered with a soft eye mask that prevented the light waves, which were emitted from the lights, from damaging the newborn's eyes.

The light waves were absorbed by the infant's skin, and broke down the bilirubin more quickly, where it would then be eliminated through the baby's stool. The baby would be turned frequently to expose different areas of its body to the lights. For more serious cases, an IV was started, and IV fluids were also given.

This was an example of how marvelous medical intervention could be, when by simply having phototherapy for a few days, an infant that otherwise may have suffered mental retardation, could go home and lead a completely normal life!

Every month we would have staff meetings to discuss anything relevant happening on the med-surg floor. As a young mother, I would often ask parenting advice of fellow nurses before, or after our staff meetings. My oldest son was a real character, and was always doing something of note. The majority of the other nurses were younger than I, and almost none of them had children yet.

The other nurses always reveled in my oldest son's latest escapades, but usually didn't have much to offer me in the way of advice. Our nurse educator who led the staff meetings, was my age. She was single with no children. At one staff meeting she stated to me that if my parenting skills were better, perhaps I wouldn't have so many problems! At first, I was a little hurt, but then I realized that she was completely inexperienced, and didn't really have a clue what it took to raise a child. (I also remembered how brilliant a parent I was, before I actually had any children!) Years later, she adopted several boys. As she was getting ready to go to church one Sunday, a neighbor knocked on her door, and asked her if she was aware of the fact that one of her boys had taken the license plates off all of the cars in their neighborhood? She said she immediately thought of me, and her comment on my poor parenting skills. The next time she saw me at work, she apologized to me for her comments that she had made to me several years ago regarding my lack of parenting skills!

Soon after I began my nursing career on the med-surg floor, I became pregnant with my fourth, and last child. I always became massively huge early on in the pregnancy, and a lot of nurses that were working with me at the time were younger and married, but had no children yet. One of those nurses later told me that she put off becoming pregnant for a while after seeing me lumbering around the hospital while hugely pregnant! One thing that is great about being pregnant, is that you can pretty much say whatever you want to, and everyone gives you a pass, because of your state of pregnancy.

One morning, there were several doctors sitting around the nursing station working on orders. One of the physicians had asked me about some lab results regarding one of his patients. I told him what the results were and they didn't make a lot of sense, but that is what they had been reported to me by the lab. When he irritatingly began to question me on how those results could even be possible, I quipped, "I don't make the news, I just report it." All of the physicians who had previously been intent looking down at their work on the desk, now looked up to see what nurse had made that sharp comment. Seeing that I was great with child, they shrugged, and went back to work! The physician I was talking to stared at me astonished for a moment, and then also continued on with his work quietly.

Heavily pregnant, I remember lumbering down to a patient's room located at the end of a long hallway, in order to give a child an oral medication. I arrived in the patient's room, only to discover that there was no cup available to put water in, so that the child could easily swallow their medication. The thought of walking all the way back to the nurse's station just to get a drinking cup was almost more than I could bear. I wondered if the child could swallow the pill dry, but decided against it. With a sigh of defeat, I trudged back down the long hallway to get a paper cup for the child to use in sipping water to take their pill, knowing I would have to trudge all the way back down to their room yet once again.

Another incident that happened while I was heavily pregnant was this: I went into a room to help a patient that was in a large crib. The room was a double, so two cribs stood side by side with only a small area in between for an emergency panel containing suction and oxygen which was mounted on the wall. Somehow, I became wedged behind one of the cribs, and was struggling to free myself. The grandparents of the child were in the room with me at the time. Alarmed, the grandmother commanded her husband to help free me by moving the large, heavy, metal crib, which he did. I was very grateful for his help.

Short of nursing staff as usual, my manager had scheduled me to work right through my due date. She had told me that all I had to do was to call a supervisor when I felt that it had become too difficult for me to continue working, and the supervisor would remove me from the schedule.

I finally decided to make the call when I was nine months pregnant. Surprisingly, a nurse I didn't know answered the supervisor's phone number. I told her that I was calling in sick for the next weekend, when I was scheduled to work. Since it was only Monday, the supervisor was confused over how I would know that I would be ill five days from then. She stated to me that I would probably be better by Saturday, and would still be able to work that weekend.

I laughed, and told her that I was nine months pregnant, and that I wouldn't be getting any better. I was a little irritated that now that I was finally making the call to stop working, I was being hassled by management. I again reiterated that I would not be coming to work on the upcoming weekend. I heard later from some of my peers that the supervisor had complained to them that night, that I had a lot of nerve calling up like that to predict that I would be unable to work on the following weekend. After making that phone call, I ended up giving birth to my son four days later — on Friday, the day before the weekend I had refused to work!

Chapter

3

During the sixteen years that I worked part-time on the pediatric med-surg floor; one case that stands out to me involved a young boy who had had his appendix out the day before. As I rounded on him at the beginning of my shift, I made a mental note that I needed to get him out of bed, and get him up walking sometime during my shift. The boy was surrounded by his loving parents, and I told the family that I would be giving their son some pain medication now, and then would be coming back in half-an-hour to get him up so he could walk. The two parents looked at each other with anxiety, and you could feel the reluctance in the air, as I made that announcement. Coming back later to get him up, the mother spoke up, and said that they "would like to respectfully decline the walk." I got the biggest kick out of that statement! I must have been unable to keep from smiling a little bit, but I told them that if they wanted their eight-year-old son to recover quickly, then this was the best thing we could do for him; and that I insisted for his own good that he needed to go for a short walk. The father hesitantly got on one side of the boy holding the boy under one of his arms, and the mother got on the boy's other side, and likewise supported her son underneath the other arm.

There stood the parents, one on each side, with their son dangling in the middle, with both of his legs drawn up high off the ground! I laughed, and told them that to count as a legitimate walk, the son had to put both of his legs on the ground and bear his own weight. The boy reluctantly did put his legs on the ground, and took a halting walk down the hall for a few minutes. I have never forgotten how cute they all were together, and have thought fondly many times over the years about their statement about respectfully declining!

One day at work, I was the nurse for a darling girl that had Down's syndrome. She was about eleven years old, and when you came into her room to give her a medication, or to do some other procedure, she would hold up her right hand blocking her face so that her face was shielded from you, and with her left hand she would silently wave you away. What a great gesture, and how often I wished that I could use the same technique with a few people I didn't want to interact with!

One evening on the medical surgical floor, a patient was admitted late at night. He was about ten years old, and laid on the bed without moving or talking. He was awake, and to look at him you didn't notice any outward signs as the cause for his distress. He was being treated at the time for leukemia and had been admitted for sores in his mouth, which were a result of his receiving chemotherapy. As I studied him, he acted as if he was severely ill. His mother was present by his bedside. At first, I thought that the boy might be faking to get attention, but the more I studied him, the more I became convinced that there was something very wrong with him, that we had not yet discovered.

As I continued to assess him, I noticed one very tiny fluid-filled vesicle on his face. I asked his mother if he had been around anyone recently with chicken pox, and she stated that of course he had! His mother apparently babysat other children for income, and several of the children in her care had chicken pox! Unfortunately, this mother either had not been educated, or didn't understand the fact that her child receiving chemotherapy would have a severely compromised immune system, to the point where even having a case of chicken pox could actually prove fatal to her son!

At that time, we had a new drug that was given IV that

could help reduce the load of chicken pox virus, and I immediately called the boy's physician. It was late at night, and I woke the physician up to let him know that I thought his patient had chicken pox. The physician immediately apologized for the fact that the boy might have chicken pox, and hung up before I could ask him for the order for the drug. I called him back again, and told him that I wanted an order for the drug that might help reduce the severity of this boy's illness. He agreed, and the drug was started that night. The boy did survive, and I was proud of being the nurse to have discovered, and intervened quickly on this boy's behalf.

Unfortunately, on the med-surg floor it was not uncommon to deal with NAT. NAT stands for non-accidental trauma, which is a clinical phrase for child abuse. Many times, the husband or boyfriend of the mother is the perpetrator for hurting the child. One day, one of my patients was an infant that had been so severely beaten, that the baby was expected to die. In this case, her boyfriend had been charged with the crime and imprisoned.

The boyfriend stated that he was innocent, but no one believed him. The young mother sat by the infant's bedside day after day. I felt so bad for her, that I decided to bring in a bouquet of dahlias that I had grown in my garden to give to her, to let her know how sorry I was for her in this terrible situation. This all happened years ago, when fresh flowers were still allowed in the hospital. Now, flowers are no longer allowed.

Not long after I had brought the young mother flowers, the young mother confessed to the authorities that it was she who had beaten the baby, and not her boyfriend! I often wondered if my bringing flowers and expressing my sorrow for her, had contributed in any way to her deciding to give her confession.

One syndrome we fortunately didn't see too often at the hospital was Munchausen's by Proxy. This was a situation where the parent or caregiver was mentally ill enough to actually make their child sick, or fake the child's symptoms, so that they as the caregiver, could get attention from the medical staff. This is obviously considered a form of child abuse, and if proven, the child would be removed immediately from the caregiver's custody.

The only way to prove that someone caring for their child in the hospital was actually the cause of their child's illness was to secretly video tape their hospital room. This would provide video proof that the parent was tampering with the child in order to produce some sort of medical result, such as putting blood in their child's diaper. Usually, the frequency of the child's hospitalizations, coupled with the fact that the lab results didn't always match the child's symptoms would lead the medical staff to wonder if a specific case could be a Munchausen's by Proxy case.

Decades ago, a female nurse was required to wear a white dress, stockings, white shoes, and a white nurse's cap. When I became a nursing student, these items still needed to be purchased and worn, but soon were considered archaic, and outdated.

After graduating from nursing school, I kept the nurse's cap. The cap sat on the top of your head and stood about five inches tall, with wings on each side of it. It was secured to your head by bobby pins which anchored it to your hair on each side.

Before each shift on the med-surg floor, report is given to the oncoming staff. Nurses from the previous shift report on the condition of each patient to the nurse coming on to that shift. As a gag, I decided to wear my nurse's cap to report one morning. I was hoping for the other nurses to stare at me like I had lost my mind, or to make funny comments about the cap. Instead, the nurses began admiring my cap, and wondering if they still had theirs somewhere at home! My joke had totally backfired on me!

I graduated from nursing school in the summer of nineteen-eighty-four, and started working in March the following year. As registered nurses, we mixed many of the drugs we gave during our shift. We reconstituted antibiotics, and it was common for us to calculate dosages. If the antibiotic drug only came in a two-gram bottle and the order was to give one-gram, we would reconstitute the dry antibiotic with sterile water, and then give half of what we had mixed up.

We also had small bottles of potassium chloride in our medicine drawers. Potassium chloride, or KCL, is an important electrolyte. We drew up the KCL in a syringe to add to the large bag of IV fluids that our patient would receive.

Ten milliequivalents, or twenty milliequivalents, were the most common amount ordered by the doctor to add to a liter bag of IV fluids. The amazing thing to me looking back now, is that potassium chloride is now kept under lock and key, and only a pharmacist is allowed to have access to it.

The reason for this is that KCL is lethal if injected intravenously. The potassium chloride we used came in small vials that looked exactly like the heparin vials containing heparin, that we would inject into children's heparin locks every four hours. A heparin lock was simply an IV that had no fluid constantly running in it, and the heparin kept the IV from clotting off, making the IV usable. I complained to the management about the fact that the two vials looked almost identical, and that something should be done to change that fact before a patient was accidentally harmed, but no change was ever made.

In all those years of flushing children's heparin locks every four hours, no nurse ever picked up the wrong vial containing KCL, which is a real testament to the diligence of all those pediatric nurses! Many years later, the practice of using heparin was discontinued, and saline was used instead. Another drug we used commonly during the winter months was aminophylline. RSV, or Respiratory Syncytial Virus was very prevalent during the months of January through May. The hospital was sometimes at full capacity with the large number of small children suffering from RSV. Aminophylline was used as a bronchodilator to help reduce the respiratory distress caused by the virus.

Our little patients were commonly put on aminophylline drips, which meant that their IV fluids were giving them a constant predicted amount of the drug. Keep in mind that as a registered nurse, I sometimes had up to thirteen children in my care, and at that time, only the RN gave medications! For each patient with RSV, an exact amount of two hours' worth of fluid would be dropped into their volutrol. The volutrol was a long plastic cylindrical chamber with measurements written on the side, that could hold one-hundred milliliters of IV fluid. The volutrol was situated below the large bag of IV fluids, and tubing below the volutrol entered the IV pump which controlled the delivery of fluid into the child's vein.

Every two hours, a dose of aminophylline would have to be injected into the volutrol and mixed with two hours' worth of fluids enabling the patient to receive a steady dose of the medication. Since each nursing shift lasted eight hours (unless we had to stay overtime), each patient required four syringes of the patient's aminophylline dose to be drawn up.

To keep up with our workload, at the beginning of our shift each nurse would fill up syringes with the correct dosage of aminophylline needed for two hours for each of their patients. Each patient would then have four aminophylline-filled syringes, which we put in a labeled dixie cup, and kept in the secured medicine room. Every two hours, we would grab the patient's syringe and refill the volutrol with two hours' worth of fluid, and add the medication.

Some of the pediatric rooms in the hospital were singles, some were doubles, and some even held four patients at a time. We had one large room where five patients could be placed, and we usually put some of the children suffering from RSV in this large room, because they all had the same disease process.

The aminophylline was very helpful in aiding in the recovery process for the children, but it had one major drawback.... over time, it broke down in the child's body to become caffeine!

Toddlers would be running laps in their cribs for hours on end! Many times, they did not sleep at night, but kept doing circles in their crib. Parents were allowed to stay with their children, and they quickly became exhausted caring for their sleepless child. I would try and encourage the parents to leave for an hour or two, knowing that without the parent, the child would most likely fall asleep, but most parents declined, not wanting to leave their ill child.

One day, I entered the large multi-patient room and the mood in the room had turned ugly, due to the exhaustion of all the parents who were trapped in this nightmare of a room. No amount of goodwill on my part was going to overcome this situation, so I quickly gave the required medication, and slowly backed out of the room!

As I have said, during the months of January through May we were caring for large volumes of babies and children with RSV. These children, especially the young babies, needed to be suctioned frequently for their copious secretions because their nasal airways were so small physically, that just even a little mucous would render them unable to breathe well. Also, very young infants breathe almost exclusively only through their nose. Many times, the infants were placed on supplemental oxygen as well. To assist with their breathing, the head of their crib bed would be elevated slightly. This allowed their lungs to expand more easily. We would place wedges under the top of their crib mattress, and rig up a sling made out of blankets that would hold the baby up in an elevated position, with the baby lying on its back. Babies would be monitored carefully, and if they became unstable, they would be transferred to the PICU. Babies and children are different from adults in many ways, but one significant difference is that they can become very ill quickly, and they can likewise, recover very quickly.

The task of suctioning fell to both the nurses and respiratory therapists. Usually, both the respiratory therapists and nurses just wore a mask, gown, and gloves when we suctioned patients. As you suctioned out your patient, you found yourself only a few inches away from their face, and the baby would frequently cough or sneeze. The result was that virus particles would fly right up into your eyes, mouth or nose! When I first started to work on the med-surg floor, I became very ill. After a while, I seemed to develop antibodies, and then I almost never became sick, as I was exposed on a regular basis to ill children's secretions.

RSV was a nasty virus even for adults. It gave you a bad cold, along with a never-ending cough that took months to resolve. Occasionally, we would discover head lice on one of our RSV patients. Head lice is not that contagious unless your head makes some sort of contact with their head. I always got a big kick out of seeing a respiratory therapist get dressed up in a gown, gloves, mask, hair cap, and eye protection when they found out the child also had head lice. Here they were on a daily basis, dealing calmly with nasty virus particles that were everywhere in the air, but yet head lice would instill such fear and trepidation on the respiratory therapist's part that it would bring them out wearing full regalia!

The hospital I worked at had a system for dealing with the bad behavior of employees which consisted of differing levels of seriousness. There were several levels, or steps, of progressive guidance; the first, being the least serious. Step two, was more serious, with step three being even more serious, and so on, until you were suspended, or finally terminated. I normally would have been mortified to have been put on a 'step one' of progressive guidance, but when I worked on the med-surg floor I found myself being put straight onto suspension one time, and it wasn't all that bad!

How I ended up on suspension was this: Back when I first began working, the nurses on the medical-surgical floor were not tested annually for tuberculosis. Later, for many years we were all tested annually for TB. Now once again at present, there is no mandatory testing for TB. Before I was aware that any TB testing had started, I received a phone call at home from a supervisor at work, wondering if I had gotten my TB test yet. I stated that I didn't know anything about it, as we had never been tested for it before. I was told by the supervisor that I did indeed know all about it, and that I was 'suspended.' I asked her, "what does that mean?" The supervisor stated, "that means that you have two weeks to get tested, otherwise you will be terminated. You also cannot come back to work until this is taken care of." Well, since I loved to stay at home even without pay, this didn't seem like such a bad deal to me! The really funny thing was that half-an-hour later, the same supervisor called me to ask if I could work the following day! I reminded her that she had just suspended me, and she sheepishly hung up. I later got tested for tuberculosis and returned to work, and was ruined from that point onward regarding progressive guidance and suspension.

I had been asked by my nurse manager if I would work sometimes as the supervisor for the med-surg floor, instead of as a floor nurse. The job consisted of carrying a beeper, and responding to the other nurse's requests for help in dealing with patients, angry parents, etc., as well as scheduling where the oncoming nurses would be assigned to work for the next shift.

It wasn't my favorite job, but I looked at it in a similar way to cleaning bathrooms in the home. Not necessarily pleasant, but someone needed to do it in order for things to run smoothly. So, I agreed to be scheduled as the supervisor sometimes.

One time, while I was acting as supervisor, a nurse called me to report that she had accidentally given the wrong dose of Trazodone. She was very upset, and so I went to look into the situation. Whenever there was a medication error, an incident report needed to be filled out by the nurse, as well as a call to the patient's physician needed to be made. The nurse was very distressed that the extra amount of Trazodone she had accidentally given the patient, would harm the patient. I comforted the nurse with my knowledge that the dose of Trazodone that she had given, would not affect her patient adversely. I happened to be very familiar with the drug, as at one point in my life, I had been put on a whopping dose of Trazodone after I had been diagnosed with breast cancer, and had become clinically depressed. The extra amount of Trazodone she had given to the child was very small.

I also remembered, and shared with the nurse about my own medication error I had made many years ago, when I accidentally gave a patient double the dose of his Demerol pain medication. I had pulled out a fifty-milligram Demerol vial, instead of the twenty-five-milligram vial. My mistake wasn't caught until later when we were counting the narcotics at the end of the shift, and I realized what I had done. The patient was on monitors because he was receiving narcotics, and had been very comfortable and pain-free my whole shift! When I made the call to the physician to notify her of my mistake, she just wanted reassurance that the patient was still doing okay, which he was. I think my reassurances to the distressed nurse helped her to feel better, and her young patient did fine with the extra amount of Trazodone he received. Medication errors happen, because nurses are human, and therefore fallible. Fortunately, patients are tough, and the errors we make usually do no lasting harm.

I had been scheduled to work as a supervisor on a weekend

that happened to be on my second child's high school graduation. I told my nurse manager that we had to talk. As I sat across the desk from her, I explained the problem, thinking she would immediately understand that I was not going to miss one of my children's high school graduation ceremonies.

Instead, she went on about how she would not be able to find anyone else to be supervisor that night, and that I would just have to come in and work that night. Upset, I thought of all my options. I knew I was going to that graduation, even if I had to call in sick. I told my nurse manager that it was against my principles to lie, but if that is what it took to right this injustice, I would call in sick. My second thought was that if I didn't get that night off, I was going to resign from being a supervisor, and never perform the job of being the supervisor again. The only reason I had been doing the job was to help the organization.

I looked at my usually nice, reasonable nurse manager, and I told her, "If I were you, I would tell me that I have that night off. Then, I would get on the phone, and see if I could find anyone to cover that night. If I couldn't, I would do the job myself." She got the point, and gave me the night off. I happily attended my son's high school graduation.

As supervisor, one of your duties was to go to the emergency room if a pediatric patient was being coded there. Your assignment during the code was to perform chest compressions. Children usually have such young healthy tissue, that their hearts usually only stop after several minutes of being deprived of oxygen. Even after their airway is occluded, or their respiratory center becomes depressed by narcotics, their heart will continue beating for several minutes after the child has stopped breathing. My experience was that if a child's heart had already stopped beating, the game was up, and the child would not be revived.

Adults, on the other hand, are quite different from children. They can have their heart stop suddenly while they are still breathing, as in a heart attack, and can be revived many times. One night in the ER, a code was called on a three-year-old child that had been involved in a car accident. The child had been sitting unrestrained in the front passenger seat. On impact, the child had been ejected through the front window of the car. The driver of the car was the child's grandmother.

After several minutes of trying to revive the child, the ER doctor called it, and we all stopped our efforts. It was later discovered that the child's neck had been broken when she went through the windshield, and her broken neck had severed her spinal cord, which had incapacitated her from being able to breathe. What a sad case!!! The police were standing by in the ER, waiting to see if the child was pronounced dead, so they could arrest the grandmother for negligence, or maybe even manslaughter. I thought to myself; that grandmother would be in her own private hell for the rest of her life, and that sending her to prison seemed to me to be ridiculous to some extent.

On one occasion, it came in very handy to be the supervisor. I received a call from my husband saying that our oldest son had been hurt, and that he was bringing him to my hospital's ER. I was able to meet both he, and my son down in the ER. I never would have had the flexibility as a floor nurse to have left my post on the ward without having someone replace me there. As supervisor, I had much more flexibility.

A blood pressure cuff had been wrapped around my son's thigh and inflated, acting as a tourniquet. A long vertical gash ran alongside his knee. The ER physician looked at the wound and said that it was beyond him. I was flabbergasted! ER doctors deal with all kinds of trauma, and this was just a laceration!

The ER physician called for an orthopedic surgeon to come in and look at the wound, because the ER doctor was afraid that a major nerve might have been cut. That morning had started with me being awoken very early by the sound of our front door being opened and shut. I jumped out of bed, and looked out a front window in time to see our oldest son, who was a character, hopping into a person's car. The person attended the same church we went to, so I wasn't alarmed. I just had no idea where they were headed off to.

The day wore on, and at two p.m. I headed off to work for my evening shift at the hospital. Later during the shift, is when I received the phone call from my husband.

It turned out that our son had gone on a church youth group hike up in the mountains. During the hike, our son had gone off the trail, and was jumping up and down on several large rocks. The rock he was jumping on gave way, and another rock tore into his leg as he fell, creating the gash alongside his knee. At first, the group tried to help my son walk back down the trail, but his leg began to bleed profusely.

Someone was sent running down the trail to get help. Park rangers came after a while, and applied the blood pressure cuff to my son's thigh, and then strapped him onto a gurney that rested on one pneumatic wheel. After being strapped multiple times onto the gurney, my son quipped that he needed to urinate. The rangers said 'no problem. We can turn you upside down in the gurney, and you can go.' My son told them that he was only joking, and the rangers proceeded to carry him down the mountain trail until they reached the parking lot. My son was driven home by church members to our house with the instructions to his father that he needed to be taken immediately to the ER, and that's where I came in.

The orthopedic surgeon later came in to my son's ER room, examined the wound, and fortunately, pronounced it to be a simple laceration with no nerve damage. The incision was sutured, and my son made a complete recovery.

Chapter
4

Tom was a nineteen-year-old who had attained his full adult size. He had severe autism, and had been admitted for having stomach problems. Usually the cut-off age for patients at the pediatric hospital was eighteen years of age, but exceptions were often made for children with disabilities.

Tom had been made npo, which stands for nil per os; Latin meaning nothing by mouth. Tom was scheduled for a procedure in the morning requiring sedation, and so the physician ordered for him to be npo.

Unfortunately, Tom could not understand why no one was letting him eat food. Tom did have an IV, and was receiving fluids through it. During my shift, Tom was becoming very agitated, and was trying to leave his room in search of something to eat. I called his doctor to get an order for a sedative, and the doctor said he would come over and take a look at Tom.

Tom would get out of his hospital bed and repeatedly leave his room in an effort to find food, with the resulting problem of pulling his IV out of his arm, as the tension became too great between Tom leaving his room to make a getaway, and the IV pole holding his bag of IV fluids being left behind!

Because of Tom's repeated attempts of leaving his room, Tom's IV had to be restarted several times. Many times, I would prevent Tom from leaving his room by pushing against the outside of the door to his room with my body weight, as Tom was trying to open the door to escape. The doctor arrived, and gave me the order for a tranquilizer. The physician sat behind the desk as I wrestled with the door, trying to keep Tom inside, with his IV intact. I was surprised that the doctor didn't come over to help me with blocking the door! Another problem we were experiencing with Tom was that if you tried to stop the six-foot tall boy, he would take a swing at you. Tom had already hit a few nurses previous to me taking over his care. Tom also liked to take off his clothes.

At one point, Tom came barreling out of his room, and miraculously the IV tubing broke, leaving the IV catheter intact in his hand! I grabbed the trailing IV tubing and bent the tubing over onto itself, in an effort to try and save the IV. Tom lumbered down the hall in search of something to eat, with me trailing behind him. As we approached another nurse's station, the ward secretary, Mary, looked up. Her eyes grew as wide as saucers at the sight of a partially-clad Tom approaching! I shouted for her to take my place holding the IV tubing, while I went into a med-room to gather supplies in an effort to salvage his IV.

I instructed Mary to just hold the IV tubing and follow Tom; but that if Tom turned towards her, to just drop the IV tubing, and get away from him, as I didn't want Mary to get hurt.

A minute or two later, I bolted out of the med-room with supplies in hand. Tom and Mary were nowhere in sight. This med-surg floor was a large, circular floor plan with three separate nursing stations. As I rounded the first corner, I could tell by the startled expressions of other patient's family members who happened to be standing in the hallway, that Tom and Mary had passed that way.

I kept thinking of how it must look to have a partially naked young man lumbering around the hallways of a pediatric hospital! I finally caught up to Tom and Mary, saved Tom's IV from being restarted, and got Tom back in his room. The decision was made to remove the door handle from the inside of Tom's room so that he could no longer get out of his room. After receiving the tranquilizer dose from the pharmacy, I gave it to Tom. Unfortunately, in some cases, there can be a paradoxical reaction. With a paradoxical reaction, you get the opposite reaction from the one you were expecting! This happened with Tom. Instead of becoming calmer, Tom became even more agitated!

Tom would stand almost naked in front of his door, frantically tapping on the window in the door, wanting to be let out. Poor Tom! There was no way to get him to understand why he couldn't eat, so that he could be sedated for his procedure in the morning.

As the night shift came on, I gave my report of the patients I had cared for to Carol, the oncoming registered nurse, with special attention and detail to Tom, and what had been happening. Carol, who thought very highly of her own nursing skills, told me that she had an outstanding relationship with Tom, and that she would just calm him down by giving him a back rub. I thought to myself, good luck with that! Carol left the room to go round on her patients, and I remained in the report room. A few minutes later, a frantic, disheveled Carol appeared, and told me that as she opened Tom's door with him standing behind it, she had put her hand on his chest to guide him back into the room, only to have been shoved aside by Tom into the wall! So much for her skill with giving back rubs! Everyone agreed that this would be Tom's last admission to the children's hospital. He would be better served in an adult setting from now on.

Most of the children staying in the hospital had at least one parent that stayed with them. We wanted to accommodate the parents, but because of space restrictions, we could only allow one fold-out bed to be provided for the parents allowing them to sleep next to their child's crib or bed. Sometimes, both parents would want to stay overnight, which meant that they had to share the one bed. Being young and healthy, and in very close proximity to each other, one can imagine what thoughts started to cross their minds. Janet, the fun nurse, was checking on a young patient one night when she accidentally lost her balance and fell onto the two parents sharing a bed; who happened to be romantically involved that night! What could she say to alleviate her embarrassment? Janet quickly stood back upright, and left the room without a word!

I was sitting at the nursing station desk one night going over some of the physician's orders. Sitting at the desk with me, was a newly-hired ward secretary, along with a male employee that had come by to visit with her.

I asked the ward secretary to perform some chore for me, and the two of them looked at each other, and then the man said, "Who made you the queen bee?" I thought for a second, and then answered, "The last time I looked, the state of Washington did." Washington was the state I was licensed in as a registered nurse. No more was said, and the task was carried out without further comment.

As nurses, we ran into all kinds of different people. One woman I remember was breastfeeding her child. We had some wonderful electric breast pumps that we supplied to any of our patient's mothers on request. Some women besides nursing their child, also pumped, and had other family members take the breast milk home, or requested that we store the breast milk in our refrigerator or freezer there at work. Their milk was put into a plastic bag, sealed, and then labeled with their name and date, and put into the refrigerator or freezer.

If the mother was unavailable to nurse the baby at the time their baby was hungry, the staff could take her saved breast milk, and use it to feed her baby.

One mother, who seemed like a very earthy type, completely caught me off-guard when, after pumping and collecting a fairly large amount of breast milk, took the milk, drank it all, and then said to me, "Waste not, want not!"

Every shift the patient's vital signs were taken. This included the heart and respiration rate, as well as what the lung sounds were. A blood pressure, and the patient's temperature were also taken. Using an electronic thermometer with a disposable plastic probe cover, there were three ways to take the patient's temperature: If the child was old enough to put the thermometer in their mouth, we could take their temperature orally; another method was to put the thermometer under the child's arm in their armpit, which was an axillary temperature. One degree was added to the resulting axillary temperature to give you the accurate temperature. The last way was to use the thermometer inside the baby's rectum. One degree was subtracted if this method was used to give you the accurate body temperature.

One evening, I was taking a baby's temperature rectally. The mother was obviously completely unaware of the rectal method to take temperatures, and assumed that I was some kind of weirdo, molesting her tiny baby! I assured her that both myself, and this method of taking a temperature were both legitimate, but I think she still had her doubts!

On the med-surg floor, most rooms were double, meaning they could hold two patients. In the center of the wall between the two cribs or beds, was a panel that had oxygen and suction available for use in case of an emergency. This central panel needed to remain clear of high chairs, balloons, toys, and all other equipment. Many times, as I made my initial rounds in the room, this panel would be blocked by all kinds of paraphernalia. I would explain to the parent why I needed everything removed, and the vast majority of parents would then quickly help me eliminate all of the items.

One day as I came into a room, the central panel was blocked with various items. I explained to the mother why I needed to be able to get to the suction and oxygen quickly, and instead of removing the items, she began to argue with me that the other nurses had let her keep those items there, and she didn't see why she should now have to remove them! I marveled that she would not want the nurse to get to potentially life-saving equipment quickly if her child needed them! As I have said before, you met all kinds of different people while working in the hospital! I did insist that the emergency panel was cleared, and the reluctant mother removed the offending items.

Many years ago, if a child broke their femur, they were put in traction for weeks to get the bone to set and then later, their leg would be put in a cast. It was common to have several patients on the med-surg floor that were in traction because the process took so long; usually several weeks went by before they could be casted. A pulley system was rigged up with ropes, and sandbags weighing various weights were then hung off the foot end of the bed. The traction kept up a constant tension on the affected leg, keeping the broken bone aligned. As a nurse, you could really see the value of good nutrition, as those patients who ate nutritious foods healed much more quickly than those that had a big jar of candy next to their bed that a sympathetic family member had given them.

A broken femur can be quite painful. Teenage boys were usually the most squeamish patients, and it was common for them to be terrified of receiving a shot containing pain medication. One day, on my rounds at the beginning of my shift, I noticed that one of my patients who was a teenage boy with his broken femur in traction, appeared to be in pain. When I questioned him, the boy agreed that his broken leg was causing him a fair amount of distress. I left and went to the medication room and prepared a syringe loaded with the appropriate amount of pain medication, and topped it with the smallest needle that could still be able to deliver the medication quickly.

When the young man saw me come back into the room with a shot, he started to freak out, and began to jump all around in the bed with his broken leg still somewhat stabilized by the traction. He stated that he now wasn't in pain. I couldn't believe that moving around like that wasn't causing him even more pain with his broken leg! As a nurse, you have to decide what really is in the best interest of your patient, which a lot of times conflicts with what your patient wants, or doesn't want to do. In this case, the young man needed the medication, and so with him twisting and jumping all around in his bed like a bucking bronco, I gave him the intramuscular injection.

After I was done giving him the injection, he calmly replied, "That wasn't so bad!" He slept in comfort throughout most of my shift.

One task I never enjoyed and found stressful, was administering chemotherapy to children. I remember one poor boy that had been through so much treatment, that he would become ill and start to throw up, just seeing me bringing his chemotherapy into his room. Zofran hadn't been discovered yet, and the anti-emetics we had weren't that great.

Parents of children stricken with cancer could be very demanding. I understood their need for control after finding themselves and their child in this terrible situation. I always tried to follow the parent's instructions to the letter if I could. They knew their child intimately, and anything I could do to help ease their burden was fine by me.

Some of the chemotherapy drugs given decades ago were particularly vile. Nitrogen mustard was still being used as a chemotherapy. We were told that if spilled, Nitrogen mustard would eat up the flooring of the hospital. I wondered to myself, why on earth are we were giving something that vile as chemotherapy?

When I became a nurse, a diagnosis of leukemia was usually a death sentence for the child. Over the years, the survival rate for children having leukemia has become quite high, which is wonderful.

Because chemotherapy drugs were so caustic, great care had to be made to ensure that the dose was exactly correct. Some chemotherapies could be filtered by the IV, while other chemotherapies were not to be filtered.

At the end of one of my shifts, my brain came up with the fact that the chemotherapy I had given earlier that afternoon could not be filtered. I, of course, had put it through an IV that did have a filter built into it. Why my brain had to tell me at this point annoyed me more than just a little. Why not give me that information before I administered the chemotherapy, instead of late at night, when I was about to end my shift?

When I called the oncologist to report what I had done, he dismissed it as unimportant. He said that the jury was still out over whether it really mattered if that particular chemotherapy was filtered or not. That made me feel a little better.

At work, I was taking care of a child with terminal cancer. As I cared for her, I could see the terrible toll cancer had taken on her small body. Normally, the child would have been sent home with hospice care, but because the mother was deemed unfit, the child remained in the hospital to allow the mother visitation with the child.

The little girl's pain was not being controlled, and this was totally unacceptable to me. I started to make calls while at work, advocating for her. Who was going to take care of this problem? I could relate all too well, as I had already had my first bout with breast cancer, and I had always assumed that once I became terminally ill, someone in the medical world would be there for me, to make sure I remained pain-free.

Finally, an anesthesiologist from the OR volunteered to be in charge of keeping her pain-free. He came up and put in an epidural line. An epidural is a small catheter that is placed in the spinal fluid of the back and analgesic medication is injected every few hours. This became the solution for this little child in relieving her pain,

I will always think very highly of that doctor! The little girl died a few days later, and I was happy for her, that her ordeal was finally over.

Occasionally, we would admit a teenage girl suffering from anorexia. Anorexic patients were hospitalized because their weight had become so low, that they were in danger of dying. They hated being at the hospital, and were being fed against their will through a nasogastric tube. They were weighed every day to ensure that they were gaining weight. The patient was weighed backwards to that she could not see what her weight was.

The water faucets in the bathroom were turned off, so that the girl could not drink a lot of water in an effort to reduce her hunger. The anorexic patients would constantly walk in circles in their hospital room, in an effort to exercise and keep their weight down. Most people, including me at the time, did not understand it. We thought—hey! If you are losing weight from not eating, just eat some food.

Many year later, after I developed breast cancer, and subsequently anorexia; I understood that for me, it was all about control in a world that had spun out of control. I now have more empathy for those girls, who were counting the days when they would be released from the hospital, and could go back to not eating, or eating very little. I now think what they really needed was some major therapy to determine the cause of their anorexia, and address that.

Over the years, many nurses came and went to work on the med-surg floor. One nurse I remember, drove me crazy every time she gave me report, because her report was always so disjointed. All of our patient's updated information was contained in a notebook, and I finally became so frustrated with her oral report, that if she was the nurse giving report, I just asked to see the report notebook, so I could read the information for myself! Needless to say, that nurse was not overly fond of me either.

One day at report, this particular nurse very proudly announced to me that she had successfully instilled forty milliliters of normal saline into a child's chest tube. The patient, a young boy, had a chest tube implanted in his left lung in order to help keep his lung inflated.

Incredulous, I looked at the nurse, and asked if she meant that she had irrigated the chest tube with the normal saline in order to keep the tube from clotting off. Irrigation would involve injecting the saline into the chest tube and then pulling the saline back out. "No," she said. She had put all forty milliliters into the lung and left it there!

"Why would you put normal saline in someone's lung?" I asked. In lungs, air is good, and fluid is bad!

She disgustedly informed me that I would see the order for the normal saline to be injected into the lung. I galloped down to the boy's room, unsure of what I would find. The boy was sitting up in his hospital bed, and didn't seem to be in any respiratory distress.

I grabbed a stethoscope and listened to his lung sounds, paying careful attention to his left side. His left lung sounded diminished and wet. I grabbed a large syringe, cleansed the port on the chest tube, connected the syringe to the chest tube, and to my amazement, was able to draw back on the syringe, and retrieve all forty cc's of fluid!

The boy's left lung sounded even better after I had eliminated all of that fluid! Sure enough, I did find the order to instill the normal saline into the boy's lung, just like the nurse had said! The order had been written by the pharmacy. One can only imagine why.

As a nurse, it is your job to refuse to carry out any order that you deem may be harmful to your patient. Any time a potential error or any other significant event happens, an incident report needs to be filled out, which I did. Not long afterwards, that particular nurse quit working there, and went back to who knows where!

After working for a while on the pediatric med-surg floor, I decided to try and become 'certified' in pediatrics. This entailed studying for a test similar to taking the state board exam, only the test would only deal with the topic of all things pediatric. Becoming certified would add prestige to myself as a nurse, as well as increase my hourly pay with an extra dollar!

I attended a study group with other nurses attempting to become certified as well. We met and took mock tests, and discussed the correct answers.

The day of the test we met in a large, secured room similar to the one we had taken our state boards in. This all occurred before computers were commonly in use! As I looked at the first question on the test, I didn't have a clue what the answer was, so I looked at the second question. No clue still! As I turned the pages, I began to realize that this test was going to be a real terror, unlike the state board exam, which I had found rather easy.

I hunkered down, and started analyzing each question. The test had been made extremely difficult in that you might know the general answer to the question, but then the question took you to even higher level of degree of difficulty in order to pick out the correct answer.

After the test, our study group met, and we started to discuss the questions, and what our answers had been. To our dismay, none of us had answered the same question with the same answer!

Amazingly, we somehow all passed! To keep our certification valid, we needed to work a certain number of hours every year in our certified field of expertise, and either take a specified amount of continuing education, or we could sit again and retake the test. I knew I personally would do whatever it took to never take that test again!

One night, I had a young boy as one of my patients. His mother was at his bedside. As I made my initial rounds on my patients for that night, the mother informed me that the boy had a medication patch on his arm, which was to keep his blood pressure from becoming too high. When I took his vital signs, the boy's blood pressure was on the low side. The mom informed me that she was sure that the patch needed to be removed, or her son's blood pressure would bottom out. Why she didn't remove it herself, is something I am still wondering over.

It was always very important to listen to any parent's concerns. The parent knew the child better than anyone else. If a parent said that their child was not acting normally, you as their nurse, had better pay close attention! In this case, I believed the mother, and I wanted that medication patch removed.

A nurse cannot change medication orders without a physician's approval. I called the boy's doctor, only to have a doctor who was on call answer the phone. He said he was not really familiar with the patient, and that he didn't want to make any changes! Disappointed, I hung up the phone. After a few minutes had gone by, I again called the doctor with my request to remove the patch. He again declined.

I called my supervisor, and we came up with the plan that if the physician refused to give me the order discontinuing the medication patch on my third phone call to him, that we would go over the physician's head, and call our medical director, and get an order from him to remove the patch.

I had my supervisor on the phone line as I made my third, and final phone call to the doctor requesting that I be able to remove the patch. Frustrated and a little angry, the doctor gave me the order to remove the patch, and we never had to involve the medical director of the hospital. The patch was removed, the skin was cleansed so that no medication remained, and the boy was fine.

Working one evening shift on the med-surg floor, one of my patients was a teenage girl. Throughout the entire shift, every time I came into the room, the girl's boyfriend would be draped all over the bed, with the girl lying there, the girl's mother at the bedside as well. As the night progressed, the mother informed me that the boyfriend would be spending the night with the girl, instead of her. I politely informed her that the boyfriend was a minor, and that we were very sorry, but that he could not spend the night with her daughter! I knew that we, as nurses, already had our work cut out for us each shift. The last thing we wanted to have to do, or be responsible for, was to watch some other person's child, not to mention that it would have been highly inappropriate.

An orthopedic surgeon had come onto the medical-surgical floor to round on one of his patients, that was also my patient. The patient had a fracture that had been repaired using a surgical pin, and had an exposed pin sticking through their skin, which wasn't uncommon. We used to routinely clean and dress the exposed pins of fracture patients with betadine gel, so that they would not become infected. The surgeon asked me if I could get him an instrument to cut the pin with, as he felt the length on this particular pin was a little too long.

I was still very new as a nurse, and after scrounging around for a few minutes, I presented him with a small pair of dikes. He looked at me in disbelief, and began to verbally berate me a little. I shrugged my shoulders, and told him that the dikes were all that I could find. He went away, and I found out later that the instrument he really wanted was a pair of bolt cutters! The bolt cutters were about one-hundred times larger than the little pair of dikes I presented to him, and could cut a pin easily without any trauma to the patient. Who knew?

Nursing is a great profession. You, as the nurse, are able to help other people who are in a very vulnerable state, and need your help. There are a vast array of jobs available to you as a registered nurse. Hospital nursing, being a school nurse, working in a medical clinic, community health nursing, home health, and hospice nursing are just a few of the jobs available to nurses. Hospital nursing alone offers many different types of jobs. Possibilities include working on the medical-surgical floor, or working in other areas, such as: cardiac, OB, ICU, PICU, NICU, OR, ER, or hospital administration to name just a few. Shifts vary to include day, evening or night, all with varying hours—typically eight, ten, or twelve-hour shifts. Staff positions also vary and include three-day positions, as well as positions where you work five days a week.

At the hospital, you can take a job as a staff nurse, where you receive benefits such as health insurance and paid vacation, or you can work per diem. Per diem means 'by the day.' With per diem, you do not receive any benefits, but in lieu of benefits, you are paid a higher hourly wage. You also have more freedom in determining what day you will work on, and may not be required to take call. Being a 'per diem' nurse worked out well for me when I started my career, as my husband's work covered my health insurance, and I wanted to work only part-time.

Some nurses become 'travelers,' or agency nurses. Theses nurses work for various agencies, and take temporary assignments at hospitals located all over the country. They usually take a six-week assignment and can extend, or they can leave, and go off to their next assignment at another locale. They are paid a tremendous wage, and the hospital also pays a stipend for their housing. If you like to travel, and are versatile, this may be a job you would love.

Some nurses go on to work in the administration of the hospital. For years, the chief executive officer of the hospital I worked at was a registered nurse. I might also add that she did a great job as the CEO.

Chapter

5

In November of nineteen-ninety-nine, I was diagnosed with breast cancer. My nursing director at the hospital was great, and quickly asked around to find out who I should see for a surgeon and oncologist. I took about eight months off from working, as I tried to recover from the surgery and chemotherapy I had undergone.

Once I had recovered sufficiently enough to return to work, my co-workers were always asking me how I was. While their intent was sincere, I just wanted to be 'normal' again, and so I began to consider working somewhere else in the hospital, where no one knew my background of having been treated for cancer.

I decided to apply for a job in the operating room at the same children's hospital I was working at. This involved being formally interviewed and accepted into a residency. I was surprised at my own choice of wanting to work in the OR, as we med-surg nurses thought that the OR nurses were a little on the mean side. Our inside joke was that they ate their young alive! We would see the OR nurses when they would come up to the med-surg floor to get their surgical patients, and have to give them a report on their patient. Now, I was interested in trying something new. I thought, why not?

The formal interview in October of two-thousand went well. I really enjoyed being interviewed, and had a good time; because I didn't really care that much if I got the job or not. The interviewing staff were a little nervous about accepting me into the residency, because since I was already an employee there at the hospital, there would be no probationary period for me, where they could get rid of me easily if they were unhappy with my performance. I was accepted into the OR residency, but before the residency even started the following January, in November I received my second diagnosis of having breast cancer.

I put a call into the nurse-educator for the OR residency. She called me right back. The nurse-educator for the residency program could sense that there was some kind of problem. She suggested that we meet at the hospital's cafeteria later that day to talk. She said that whatever the problem was, we could work it out. I thought to myself, she will be blown away when I tell her I have cancer!

Later that day, I met with the nurse-educator. She was speechless when I told her that I had breast cancer, and that I would be undergoing radiation, surgery, and probably chemotherapy.

I suggested that I proceed with the residency, but not be paid for it. That way, if I could not complete the residency due to being ill, there would be no hard feelings. She told me that the hospital needed to pay me for my hours while I was in the residency, and that they still wanted me, which I thought was very generous of them. We decided together that in January of two-thousand-and-one, I would go ahead and begin my residency as planned, and see how it went.

In November of two-thousand, my radiation treatments began. I had more surgery in December, with radiation treatments resuming a couple of weeks after surgery. My OR residency began in January, and I went down every day for the final four radiation treatments during my lunch hour. The workers in the X-ray department were really surprised when I showed up in my OR scrubs and cap! None of the other nurses in my residency class knew anything about my cancer or treatment.

The residency was very interesting. Here I was, a registered nurse with sixteen years of med–surg experience, and yet the residency would last for several months! Why it would take so long to teach me what I needed to know to work in an OR remained a mystery to me. The OR residency was a wonderful diversion for me as I began yet another course of chemotherapy for my cancer recurrence.

As nurses in training, we all met together for several weeks in the morning for classes. We learned a few of the basic instruments used in surgery, along with the roles performed in the operating room. Later, I found it overwhelming when I finally realized the vast number of all the different operations there were, the different types of OR tables that patients were placed on, along with the various instruments, medications, implants, etc.

The role of the registered nurse in the operating room is usually to be the 'circulator.' The main role of the circulator is to be the patient's advocate while the patient is anesthetized on the operating table, and is so vulnerable.

The minimum staff in the operating room include the surgeon, anesthesiologist, scrub technician, and the circulator. The circulator is always a registered nurse. The scrub person can be an RN, or a scrub technician. Although the group acts as a team, the circulator is actually the person in charge of the operating room. This seemed odd to me, as there are two doctors in the room with her (I will refer to the circulator as a her, even though I recognize that there are male registered nurses who perform the job of circulator).

The circulator interviews the patient before surgery, making sure that the patient's history and consent match what the patient is telling them. If there are any concerns along the way, the circulator makes sure that those concerns are addressed and resolved before the patient is brought back to the OR room.

While the patient is anesthetized, it is up to the circulator to ensure that her patient receives the best of care, and that nothing untoward occurs. She makes sure that the patient hasn't eaten or drank anything that would keep the surgery from   proceeding. The danger in a person having eaten before surgery is that food could still be in their stomach creating the possibility of the patient later throwing up, and aspirating food into their lungs. Understanding any health issues, past surgeries involving metal implants or pacemakers, whether the patient has dentures or hearing aids; plus ensuring that any metal jewelry has been removed, are all part of the circulator's interview process with the patient. During surgery, cautery is commonly used, and metal jewelry left on could attract the electricity used during the surgery, and burn the patient in the spot where the jewelry was. I personally have never seen this happen, even though some patients insist on wearing rings, piercings, and earrings. Not removing your jewelry before your surgery will however, stress out your circulator!

The circulator at the children's hospital where I work at brings the patient back to the OR room. The circulator positions the patient, and places the oxygen saturation monitor, the blood pressure cuff, temperature probe, and the EKGs on the patient. For pediatric patients, an IV is also started by the circulator in the OR room while the child is given some anesthetic agent via a mask.

Next, the circulator assists the anesthesiologist with intubating the patient. Once that is achieved, the circulator rechecks the positioning of the patient and a cautery grounding pad is placed by the circulator to prevent the patient from being burned by the cautery that is going to be used. Some form of heating blanket is placed on the patient to keep them warm during the operation. The circulator is also responsible for putting on sequential compression devices (SCD'S) on the lower legs if they are warranted, depending on the age of the patient, and the length of the operation. If a foley catheter needs to be placed before the surgery begins, it is also the circulator's job.

The circulator then preps the area to be operated on. Sometime before the operation begins, she is also responsible to count sponges, sharps, and possibly instruments with the scrub person. Instruments need to be counted if an 'open' case is done, where a large enough incision in the body is made where an instrument could be placed inside a body cavity.

The count is put on a white board at the back of the operating room. A 'time-out' is performed by the circulator before the operation begins. This consists of the circulator announcing to the room the name of the patient, their medical record number, their weight, the operation to be performed, whether antibiotics have been given to help fight infection, and any allergies the patient may have. Everyone in the room must agree with the information before the procedure begins. Any potential concerns can also be brought up. Also, if any of the staff is unfamiliar with each other, it is up to the circulator to have each person introduce themselves.

During the operation, the circulator assists the surgeon by obtaining and opening any sterile instruments or implants that the surgeon deems necessary during the operation. She is also responsible for all the people in the room participating in the surgery to be dressed appropriately with masks and eye protection, and ensuring the sterility of the operating area known as the 'field.' The circulator also makes a record of the operation. Years ago, this was done with paper and pen, but now it is done electronically. She labels any specimens that are taken, and before the end of the surgery, the circulator and scrub technician count again, making sure that they have all the sponges, sharps, and instruments that they started with. After the surgery, the circulator and anesthesiologist take their patient to recovery where a report is given to the RN doing the recovery.

There is always a circulator in the room with the patient. If the circulator needs a break or lunch, another RN comes into the room to stay with the patient. The same is true for the scrub person being replaced during a break by another scrub person.

While I was still a resident, one of the best examples I remember of the circulator being the patient's advocate, was that during an earthquake we had that shook and rocked the OR suite, the circulator threw her body over the anesthetized patient's head to protect him!

While I was still in training, I happened to be in the OR with my instructor while together we performed the role of the circulator. The surgical technician was a beautiful young girl, who had a dark exotic look. The surgeon and anesthesiologist were practically melting on the floor as they talked to her. I looked at my instructor who was also in her forties as I was, and asked her, "When did we become chopped liver?" She quickly replied, "about twenty years ago," at which we both laughed hysterically, back in our corner of the room!

After a few weeks of our residency, we were allowed to shadow a real circulator, and learn what it was like to be in the OR. Even though I spoke English as my native language, at first, I could not understand what was being said in the OR. I could hear the syllables, but it was like a foreign language to me. For instance, 'I want a farr straight up' meant, I want a certain type of retractor right away. Also, the pace of the OR was very fast.

One very funny story regarding language in the OR was this: One of the other four residents was a Korean nurse, and her name was pronounced Mesue. One morning, she was in the OR, and her circulator left the room for a few minutes. The surgeon turned to her and said, "too-me." She said, "no, Mesue." He again repeated the word, "too-me." She again repeated, "Mesue." He then stated, "Look girlie, I don't want to play word games with you." What the surgeon wanted was a toomey syringe. Mesue, of course, had no idea what he was talking about. When the residency group met together later that afternoon, Mesue related the story to us. Most of us laughed so hard that we cried. Mesue however, did not find the incident that amusing, and she dropped out of the OR residency, and went back to the nursing job she had before she came into the residency. I loved being in the OR. I loved the fact that I was treated like a regular person, since only the management knew the back story of my being treated for cancer.

After several weeks, we finished the classroom portion of the OR residency class, and we spent all of our time in the operating room with an experienced circulator. I saw an interesting case where the gallbladder was being removed laparoscopically. Several stab wounds were made to the abdomen, and a scope was placed down one of them. Monitors above the OR bed projected what the camera, mounted onto the scope, was looking at. It was a little like being Alice in Wonderland going down the rabbit hole! Inside the abdomen was surprisingly colorful.
Human fat was yellow, and the liver looked just like the liver you would buy at the store! Other instruments were placed in the other stab wounds, and you could watch the surgeon ligate all the blood vessels surrounding the gallbladder. The gallbladder was then captured in a tiny bag and brought up and pulled out through one of the small incisions. Very interesting!

They were short-staffed in the OR, so they pulled the nurse-educator and I to cover a room. We had a blast being together. She was extremely funny, so we had a really good time together. We told both of the doctors (the surgeon and the anesthesiologist) that what we lacked in technical skill we made up for in enthusiasm! They weren't sure what to make of that! I also got to start a lot of IV's, and learn how to put the circuit (tubing) on the ventilator machine, which is changed out for each patient before the next case.

One morning while still in the residency, I went to work in the OR room I was assigned to. Unbelievably, it was a room where a woman was there for breast reconstruction after having had a right mastectomy! She was also having her left breast augmented; or added to. Her case struck home with me, as I wished I too, could have a right breast again. However, I had decided against reconstruction, because I just couldn't reconcile myself with having a breast implant.

During the surgery a few times, I thought I would have to leave the room, because I might start crying. I'm sure that would have impressed everyone in the OR room, who had no idea about my cancer! They would have thought I was a real psyche-case for sure! During the case, I kept thinking, what lesson is God trying to teach me here that I was just not getting?

Then our next case was......would you believe it? A woman having her silicone breast implants removed because the implants had ruptured. Talk about a terrible case! The surgeon spent forever picking out little pieces of silicone. There was no way the surgeon could ever remove it all, as there were tiny pieces of silicone everywhere. That case cured me from feeling bad about not having a breast reconstruction.

My residency course was almost finished! April fifteenth would be our last day with our nurse educator, and we were going to SORELY miss her! As residents, we had all passed our competency tests for working in the OR. From April fifteenth, to July fifteenth, we would be on 'orientation,' where another experienced circulator would work alongside us in various cases. After that, we would be completely on our own as the circulator in the room! I had also applied for, and had accepted to work a permanent eight-hour, three-day-a-week position working with children in the OR.

For the first time in sixteen years I would be a staff nurse, instead of working per diem! I was very excited about starting to receive benefits such as health insurance and paid vacation.

Chapter

6

When I first started to work in the OR as a regular staff nurse, one of the problems I encountered frequently was that because the physicians didn't know you, they were hesitant to have you for their circulator. One morning, an anesthesiologist and I went together to collect a child from the Pediatric Intensive Care Unit, or PICU, so the child could be brought down to the OR to have surgery. While we were together in the elevator with the ill child, the anesthesiologist asked me if I was nervous. I stated, "Not at all." He inquired why that was. I said, "Because I have you with me!" When you work on the med-surg floor you do not have the luxury of having a super-qualified doctor at your side. On the med-surg floor the registered nurse is at the top, in the hierarchy of staff available! If your patient decides to tank, it is all up to you to take care of the situation. You can call for help of course, but until help arrives, you, as the RN, are in charge of the problem; which can be quite stressful. Working in the OR with at least one physician, and usually two, made emergencies so much easier to deal with.

When I first began to work in the OR, I had a fixed schedule; and I worked every Tuesday, Wednesday, and Thursday. Every Tuesday morning, I worked with Dr. S., the ophthalmologist. On Wednesday morning I worked with Dr. R. and his partner, who were both ENT physicians.

On Thursday mornings, I worked with Dr. G., a urologist. All of these surgeons had blocks, or groups of surgeries in the morning; starting at eight and running until around noon. Every week I worked those same three days, and usually always with the same surgeons. In the afternoons, a group of pediatric general surgeons had their blocks of surgeries, and I worked frequently with all of them as well. Many local dentists also had blocks of surgeries that would be scheduled to fill in any of the gaps remaining in the OR schedule.

All of our larger pediatric cases were done in the main OR, and all of our smaller day surgery cases were done in the older children's hospital which was located across the street from the larger hospital. My favorite area to work in was in the children's day surgery area. The children were usually healthy, and the pace was very quick.

The children's day surgery area ran like a well-oiled machine. One RN, called a facilitator, picked up the patient from the pre-surgery area where the child had been admitted. The young patient and their parents were brought by the facilitator to one of the two holding rooms which were located close to the two OR suites. There, in the holding room, the surgeon, anesthesiologist, and the circulator could talk to the parents concerning their child's health, and the operation that was about to take place.

When the OR room was ready, and the consent, and history and physical (H&P) were complete, the child was brought back to the OR room, and the parents were sent out to the surgical waiting area. Once the operation was completed, the child was taken to the recovery room, which was only a few feet down the hall from the OR rooms. Report was given to the recovery room nurse by the circulator and anesthesiologist. If the operation being performed on the child in the OR was a short one, the RN facilitator would have already picked up the next patient and brought them back to the holding room.

As the patient left the OR room, staff would quickly clean and turnover the room, readying it for the next patient. This enabled the day surgery area to complete as many as eight to ten surgeries before noon, with the first case starting at 8 a.m.

Some examples of these type of cases were: ENT cases such

as tonsillectomies, adenoidectomies, ear tube placements, tympanoplasties, and nasal cautery. Hernia repairs including umbilical, and inguinal hernias common in premature infants, were also performed frequently by the pediatric surgeons. Eye cases, such as tear duct probes, chalazion removal, strabismus repairs, as well as occasional cataract removals, were done. Other cases included cyst removals, and urology cases such as circumcisions, orchiopexies, and hypospadias repairs were done frequently. Dental restorations were also done routinely by many local dentists.

We had so much fun working together that Dr. G., the urologist, and I would often comment that we would almost do the job for free!

I had a new boss in the OR, and I got to use a fun line that I never got to use very often. While we were in a case together, I asked her, "Do you know about me?" That question will always get a hesitation from the person you are asking the question to, while they wonder if they really do want to 'know' about you! Ha!

After staring at me for a few seconds, she shook her head no, so I took her into a corner of the OR room, and told her about my situation of receiving chemotherapy for cancer. She was floored…but then recovered, and was very supportive.

The fun part of working in the OR, especially in the day surgery area, was the camaraderie between all the staff. We were good at what we did, we all liked each other very much, and occasionally, we would become a little irreverent. Patients, I think, expect a team in white to all be standing around very seriously. Hearing music playing when they enter the OR, and the staff joking around might be a shock to most patients. That though, is a good sign that your team is in great form. On the other hand, if it is quiet and somber, that may mean one of two things. Either things are not going well, or there is some kind of disagreement between the staff.

I did sometimes work in the main OR with some of the more serious cases that required a larger set-up, and after their surgery, the children would then be hospitalized. Some examples of large cases I worked in included orthopedic cases involving broken arms or legs where an incision was made, and plates, screws, rods, or wires were installed.

Spinal fusion cases for children with scoliosis were huge cases involving straightening out a severely curved spine, and lasted several hours. Spinal fusion cases required a much larger set-up than the smaller cases. Besides all the usual monitors and IV fluids that were commonly used in cases, an arterial line needed to be started by the anesthesiologist before the operation could begin.

The art-line was difficult to start, as arteries are much harder to find than veins. The anesthesiologist would palpate the anesthetized patient's upturned wrist, feeling for a pulse. Then the anesthesiologist would place an IV catheter inside the artery. Because the arteries were difficult to access, this procedure alone usually took at least half-an-hour to complete. The art-line tubing was filled with normal saline and hooked up to transducers that were connected to the anesthesia machine. The art-line could monitor the patient's blood pressure precisely during the long multi-hour procedure.

Cell-saver machines were also used, where the blood suctioned during the case was collected, filtered, and then cleaned at the end of the case. The resulting blood would then be given back to the patient. These cases usually required the patient to have been typed and crossed before the surgery began, so that extra blood, if needed, was available to be given during the surgery.

Because the surgeon was working near the spinal cord, a spinal monitoring technician would apply little electrodes on the patient in various locations at the beginning of the case, so that nerve function could be monitored throughout the operation. If a change in nerve function was detected during the surgery, the surgeon was notified by the technician, and the surgeon could then readjust the metal rods and wires used in straightening out the spine.

Craniotomies were also large cases that were performed. Children with tumors in their head, or children with trauma to their head were the usual reasons a craniotomy needed to be performed. The patient would be sent to the PICU afterwards, especially if they required an external drain in their head that had to be monitored afterwards. The temporary drain had to be kept at a certain level relative to the patient's head. If the external drain was placed too low below the head, it could cause cerebrospinal fluid to drain out which could cause the brain to herniate, and the patient could die!

Hydrocephalus is a condition where there is an abnormal buildup of fluid in the brain. This condition may be congenital, but is also commonly seen in 'Shaken Baby Syndrome.' This syndrome happens when an angry parent violently shakes a young baby. The baby's head whips back and forth injuring their brain, causing bleeding and swelling. If left untreated, the head of the infant can grow grotesquely large. The child may also exhibit 'sunset eyes' where the eyes are forced to look down towards the nose because of the increased pressure in the head.

For hydrocephalus, a shunt system needs to be implanted to drain the excess fluid from the head into the abdomen. The drain, called a ventriculoperitoneal, or VP shunt, allows that excess fluid inside the head to drain into the abdomen where it can be reabsorbed by the body. I once had a patient when I worked on the med-surg floor who was a little girl around two-years old. She had a severe case of hydrocephalus caused by abuse. She had the appearance of a Martian with her huge misshaped head, and only the whites of her eyes showed, because her pupils had been forced downward by the increased pressure in her head!

She had surgery, and I was lucky to be able to see her a few years later. She had become a very attractive little girl with curly hair--looking completely normal! The change in her appearance was both amazing, and wonderful!

One day, I went in for my chemotherapy, and was sitting in the waiting room with the other patients. I thought the oncology clinic I went to was somewhat bizarre, as the oncology physicians had combined with another group of infectious disease physicians that treated patients with infections that were not responding to normal treatment. That left immunocompromised patients who were taking chemotherapy sitting with other patients that had the worst infections in the county, which had not responded to standard antibiotics! While I waited, I noticed one of the surgeons I worked with in the OR was also there. I knew that Dr. P. had been battling a severe sinus infection for months without cure. He was an older man, and very prideful. Dr. P. never acknowledged knowing me while we sat in the waiting room, but to be fair, he might have just been respecting my privacy. I know that is why I didn't say anything to him. When they called out his name, they butchered the pronunciation of it. He rose up commandingly, and informed them of the correct pronunciation. They could have cared less. Welcome to the other side of treatment!

Next, they called out for Susan Johnson. I stated, "I am Sheila Johnson." They said, "yea, that's right, come on back." Hey, I thought, I am here for chemotherapy, and I sure don't want to get someone else's concoction of drugs! It was quite an education for me to be a long-term patient, and experience the vulnerability that patients feel when they find themselves in serious medical situations.

While at work in the OR, I found myself becoming more and more fatigued from my repetitive, weekly chemotherapy treatments. I also found myself becoming more emotional than usual. None of the staff in the OR were aware of my ongoing cancer treatments. During one case involving a child, the child coded and everyone sprang into action. During the code, the pharmacist who arrived to help with the code was rude to me. After the child was coded successfully, and everyone had relaxed a bit, I started to cry a little. The OR staff was somewhat astonished at this, but the anesthesiologist stated kindly to me that codes can sometimes be very stressful. I told him, "I am not crying because of the code. I am crying because someone was mean to me." Afterwards, about three people came up to me separately and apologized for being mean, none of whom was the pharmacist!

When I first started to work in the OR in 2001, angry empowered surgeons were definitely on their way out. It had become politically incorrect for anyone to throw their weight around by having fits, or throwing things. A few surgeons still remained who were caught in the changing times, and who, after behaving badly, were then asked to go to anger management classes. I was told that the surgeon had to pay for their own classes, which I was told cost several thousand dollars. Afterwards, they were put on probation, and emails were circulated to the staff for months asking for their input on what the surgeon was now like to deal with.

When I first began working in the OR, I had quite an experience with a surgeon. For each operation, the surgeon has to have two things in order for the surgery to take place. One, is a consent that is dated within thirty days, and is filled out properly stating the correct operation, the correct side if that is an issue, and signed by both the surgeon, patient, or patient's parent if they are a minor, and a witness. The second thing is the patient has to have a current history and physical, or H&P, filled out by the surgeon. It is one of the circulator's jobs to make sure that both are present, as well as that the information matches with what the patient is telling the circulator in their interview.

I was still extremely inexperienced, and when I asked the

surgeon a question about his history and physical for the patient, he blew up, and ripped me verbally up one side and down the other. He really got to me, and I began to cry. Afterwards, when I went home, I thought I have to come up with a plan so that I am never put in that situation again. The plan I came up with was this: I decided that if any surgeon wanted to get nasty with me, I would speak his name sternly in an effort to get him to stop, and if he didn't stop, I would call in the charge nurse, write an incident report, and if I wrote a surgeon up three times, I would refuse to work with that surgeon anymore, telling the hospital that they had failed to protect me from a 'hostile environment.' As it happened, the very next week I was again doing another case with the same surgeon who had made me cry. He started in on me again, so I said his name in a very warning tone, and he backed down, apologized, and I never had another problem with a surgeon yelling at me again. Planning is empowering!!! I would also tell the new OR nurse residents my story, in an effort for them to see that they do not have to put up with anyone's bad behavior.

Occasionally, I would be involved with an adult case in the OR even though I was a pediatric nurse. One day, we had a case where a woman had been kidnapped for two weeks, and raped. She was so traumatized that she was non-verbal. We took her back to the OR for a procedure, and I was astonished at how completely filthy she was. She had some abrasions on her legs that had been dressed with some topical medication, and then bandaged. It made me so angry that another nurse had not given her what she needed most; and that was a long, hot bath. It was a joke to apply medication and bandages to wounds on someone that filthy! Also, a lot of medical students had come into the OR room during her case to watch, which upset me as well.

I was still seething over that case when I returned to my OR room to ready it for our next patient, which was a tiny baby.

At that time, we used real linen sheets to dress the bed in the OR. When I returned to the room with the linen sheets in my hands, there was the OR bed all dressed out in new paper bedding that we were switching over to; with the two reps for the paper bedding standing proudly alongside the bed. They had also placed two arm boards dressed in paper coverings along the sides of OR bed as well, which of course, I would not need for a little baby.

I told them I didn't need the arm boards, and they told me that I didn't understand, even though they were the ones who didn't understand! At that, I lost it, and threw the linens that I held in my hands down on the floor, and shouted, "This stupid OR!" and started to cry.

Everyone scattered and ran to get management, who came quickly to the room. They, of course, knew that I was being treated for cancer, and asked me what they could do for me. I told them I wanted everyone, especially the paper-reps to clear out of my room, and stay out! This was accomplished quickly. After a short while, I realized it was not really the paper-reps that had set me off, as much as my anger for the previous case. I was mad that no nurse had bathed that poor woman, and was disappointed in myself as well, that I, as the circulator, had allowed so many people to come into the room to watch her procedure.

I decided that I needed to apologize to the reps, which I did. Afterwards, every time I came out of my room and the two paper-reps saw me, they would run up to me, and reconfirm that there were no hard feelings. I thought to myself you both had better cool it, or you will both get a second round of my rage inflicted upon you!

That woman's case remained at the back of my mind for years; and years later, I was involved with another adult patient. He was a man who had cut his fingers badly with a saw. His injured hand was absolutely filthy. After he was asleep on the OR table, I filled a large basin full of warm, soapy water, and began to scrub his filthy hand before he had surgery. I took my time to clean his hand, and would have defied anyone to try and stop me! I thought of that woman's case as I scrubbed the man's hand clean, and felt somewhat vindicated. The surgeon commented on how happy he was to see me clean his patient's hand so thoroughly before he began the surgery!

When I was still quite new to the OR, but was on my own as a circulator, the surgeon I was working with was performing a major ear surgery. As the surgery started to come to a close, I wondered if the surgeon was going to leave the two tiny sponges called cottonoids in the ear. So, I asked him. Both he and the scrub-tech stared at me in astonishment. I thought that maybe it was a super dumb question, but it turned out that they had both forgotten the two sponges were in there! The surgeon announced: "Well, that is just as the safeguards are supposed to work!" The two cottonoids were removed, and the final count was correct. I was rather pleased with myself.

After working for a while in the OR, I found that some of the patients viewed the anesthesiologists as not even being medical doctors! It is true in some settings that a nurse anesthetist might be the one administering anesthesia, but at our hospital only medical doctors who had gone through a rigorous residency for anesthesia were used. I viewed them as being similar to critical care doctors. They were well versed in how to deal with all kinds of patient emergencies, including extensive knowledge on how to maintain a patient's blood pressure, heart rate, etc. In my opinion, they seemed to especially thrive, and really excel in emergent cases, many times working together with other anesthesiologists, in cases where the patient had become unstable, and critically ill.

I found that it was true that a patient rarely died in the operating room; mainly due to the anesthesiologist's skill at keeping patients alive through their repertoire of drugs, their ability to maintain an airway, give blood, plasma, and other fluids, so that the patient almost always left the OR alive.

One patient I remember, was a teenage boy, that had been shot in a gang rivalry. He was in such bad shape with multiple gunshot wounds to the abdomen, that no one expected him to live. A vascular surgeon had been called in to try and stop the bleeding. The surgeon patched up some of the major bleeds, and knowing that the patient wasn't likely to survive a long procedure, actually packed the boy's abdomen full of sterile towels, and then sewed up his towel-filled abdomen together using an empty sterile IV bag! The IV bag was used as an extension for his skin at the incision sight, because the skin edges were unable to meet together, with all of those towels packed inside. I was thrown as the circulator as to how to record all of that in my report. Usually, it is my job to ensure that nothing is left in the patient, and here we had just packed the patient full of towels!!! Throughout the operation the anesthesiologist had been infusing several units of blood into the patient, and as we transferred the patient up to the PICU, you could see the patient's abdomen swelling as the blood we were putting in was coming right out through all of his gunshot wounds back into his abdomen. I was sure glad I wasn't the intensive care nurse that night that was receiving him as a patient! None of us thought that the patient would survive, and yet he did! He later came back for more surgery, and had all of the towels that were left in his abdominal area removed!

One morning in September two-thousand-and-one, as I drove to work, I heard on the radio that a plane had just hit one of the twin towers in New York. In my mind I could picture a private pilot having a medical emergency with his small light plane, and hitting the building, doing minimal damage to the building. It wasn't until I arrived at the hospital and watched more news reports, that I found out that the plane involved was actually a large commercial plane, and that a second large commercial plane had just hit the second tower as well. Unbelievably, terrorism had arrived on America's own shores. No one in their wildest imagination, could predict what would happen next, as both structures collapsed, killing many of the occupants and first responders. We felt sheer disbelief as information continued to unfold throughout the day. It is still hard to comprehend what happened on the eleventh of September those many years ago, as I write this.

Chapter

7

Times had been changing in the medical world for the last several decades. Office costs for a private practice surgeon had become very high. One surgeon told me that he paid twenty-two-thousand dollars a month just to run his office! Also, reimbursements from many insurance companies along with Medicare, had been on the decline for quite a while. It was hard for private practice physicians to enjoy being on a vacation for longer than a week or two each year, because they wouldn't be bringing in any money during that time, and yet their office costs remained fixed. Liability insurance premiums costs had become very expensive as well.

Because of those reasons, a lot of surgeons prior to the Affordable Care Act (aka Obamacare) had decided to become an employee of the hospital. The advantages to the doctor were that besides receiving a monthly wage, the hospital paid for the surgeon's office costs including their staff, as well as the surgeon's liability insurance premiums. The disadvantages to the surgeon were, that if you didn't like your office staff, you could no longer fire them, and you had to jump through any hoops that the hospital required of you. By the year two-thousand-and-fourteen, only two of the surgeons that I frequently worked with remained independent from the hospital, having their own private practices.

Is it a conflict of interest if a hospital has most of the physicians and surgeons in town actually working for them as employees? Is it unfair if the hospital-employed physicians tend to refer their patients to other hospital-employed doctors? You be the judge.

One reason I wanted to write this memoir, is that I can see that the Affordable Care Act now seems to get a significant amount of blame for all of medicine's woes; when in fact, healthcare had been in a declining free-fall for years, with health care costs spiraling out of control. Decades before the Affordable Care Act, my family practice doctor had banned together with several other family practice doctors. Because of those same reasons of high liability costs, high office rents, along with having to pay employee's salaries and benefits, coupled with poorer reimbursements from insurance companies, the private practice physicians had banned together to cut costs, and to pool their reimbursements. That way, the payments received could be divided up between them, and hopefully each individual doctor would be able to rely on having a steady monthly income.

Dr. M., a very sweet anesthesiologist, was talking about how he had met his wife who worked in the OR. He said that he had decided early on, that he didn't want to date anyone from the OR, but that his future wife was so interesting and nice, that he decided to make an exception. Already knowing why, I asked him what he meant by that statement of not wanting to date someone who worked in the OR. Now, Dr. M. realized his mistake, and yet there was no way out of it. There is a saying that the nurses in the operating room 'eat their young alive.' While there are many lovely, sweet people that work as nurses in the OR, the majority of us, including myself, are not sweet wilting wallflowers! We know how to take care of ourselves, and we have no problem facing conflict with a surgeon, if we need to help our patient. Knowing all of this, and being merciless, I continued to teasingly ask Dr. M. what he meant by that statement......? He stammered and stuttered, until I finally quit teasing him!

In a hallway outside the main OR, sits a bench where prison guards sit and wait while their prisoners undergo surgery. The first time I encountered a prisoner was just after I had started working in the OR. Going in to interview my male patient, I noticed another man sitting next to him. Both were clean and well groomed. I assumed that they were partners, and that the non-patient male was there in support of his partner. When I explained to the non-patient male where he would go to wait for the patient, he said "no," but that he would stay with the prisoner until he was anesthetized, and then he would take off the prisoner's shackles. My eyes must have grown as wide as saucers at this statement, because working almost exclusively with children, I had never encountered a prisoner before! I was also amazed that the prisoner was so well groomed. I can only imagine that he must have been incarcerated for a white-collar crime!

Another episode involving a prison guard was that one morning, I came to work and went into our lounge. The staff lounge is large and very nice. In the lounge are tables and chairs, two refrigerators to keep our lunches in, a coffee maker, microwave, sink, and a small sofa with chairs around a large wide-screen TV. It is a much nicer lounge than the one on the medical- surgical floor, where I had worked previously. On the medical-surgical floor the lounge was a tiny room with a couple of chairs, one table, and no television at all! I think the difference in lounges was due to the fact that the OR generates a lot of income for the hospital, so working there, you seem to get more perks than the average worker.

I digress. One morning, I came into the lounge, and two of the nurses were talking angrily about a prison guard who wouldn't leave the OR to go sit on 'the bench.' This guard insisted on staying with the patient (his prisoner), and the nurses didn't like that he was so assertive. They also felt that he shouldn't be in the room while the operation was taking place. The more the nurses talked about the offending guard, the more I realized that the guard was probably my son! I decided to keep my mouth shut about the relationship I had with the guard. When I talked later to my son about the episode, he confirmed that he was the prison guard there at the OR that day! The funny thing is that not one of those nurses would have ever dreamed that that guard was my son! How often do we find ourselves in a similar situation, where the odds are astronomically against a person we are talking about being related to someone else within hearing distance, and yet it happens not infrequently. The other nurses still do not know to this day that the guard was my son!

Before a surgical case began, I interviewed the mother of my patient, and explained to the mother where she would wait while the surgery was taking place, as well as how and where she would eventually be reunited with her child. The mother was concerned that there might be an emergency involving her child while the child was in the OR room. She asked me if I would immediately call her if there were any problems with her child while we were back in the OR. This question took me by surprise for a moment, as I thought of what my answer to her would be. Finally, I told her the truth. I told her, "no, I would not be calling you, but I would be doing everything in my power to reverse any adverse situation we found ourselves in with your child." She seemed satisfied with my answer, even though I could not fulfill her request. Her child went on to have their operation without incident.

In the morning before work begins, the nurses and surgical technicians gather in the lounge to watch TV, chat and eat breakfast. Sometimes, a staff member will make a treat for the group and bring it in. Any food left on the table in the lounge is fair game for all to eat. One morning, one of the male anesthesiologists brought in some bread he had made. He was dressed very smartly in street clothes. One of the nurses who is very sweet and without guile, said to him, "You look really good in clothes!" We all burst out laughing and Lisa, the nurse who had made the statement, turned beet red. The anesthesiologist waited for the laughter to die down and then said, "You should see me without my clothes on!" At this, another round of laughter exploded in the room. One of the best things about working in the OR is the camaraderie between all the workers. We aren't with the patients long enough to develop deep relationships with them, but we spend hours with the OR staff, and get to know and like each other very much.

When I first came to work in the OR, I began to work with Dr. R. who was an ENT, or Ear, Nose and Throat, surgeon. Dr. R. is extraordinarily smart, is very serious many times, and he possesses a lively dark wit. For some reason, he and I did not hit it off well at the beginning. We never verbalized our dislike for each other, and yet we found ourselves working fairly frequently with each other. Dr R. has two morning blocks each week where he usually performs around nine cases in the morning, and is finished around twelve or twelve-thirty in the afternoon, before his clinic hours start at one p.m.

One day as I was assigned to be Dr R.'s circulator, the scrub-tech I was working with dropped the package of ear tubes she needed to use for our first case of the day which was a bilateral myringotomy with tubes. A bilateral myringotomy with tubes, or BMT, means this: bilateral, refers to both ears, and myringotomy is the act of putting a hole in the ear drum, while the 'T' stands for the ear tubes placed in the incision. This procedure is performed frequently on children, usually fairly young ones, to help eliminate the recurring ear infections they have been having.

If you have an inner ear infection, pus and debris builds up inside the middle ear, causing pressure and pain. If left untreated, the tympanic membrane or eardrum, will finally rupture, giving relief from the pain, and drainage will be seen on the outside of the ear. The problem with letting nature take its course like this, is that every time the tympanic membrane ruptures and then heals, it builds up scar tissue, which eventually can inhibit your hearing ability.

To alleviate this condition from happening, the surgeon makes a small incision in the tympanic membrane, and inserts an ear tube which is a tube with an open end on both sides. The ear tube straddles the tympanic membrane, allowing the pressure in the outer and middle ear to equalize. Usually, your eustachian tubes keep the pressure of the middle ear equal to the outer air pressure. However, in young children, their eustachian tubes are narrower, and can become blocked more easily. As children get older, their eustachian tubes become larger and allow the outside pressure and the middle ear to equalize. That is why it is much rarer to see an adult come in needing ear tube placement.

Ear plugs need to be worn any time the child is in water, because you don't want any water getting into the middle ear via the ear tube. This particular morning, as we set up for our first case for the day, I had determined that Dr. R. was not in the OR room yet. I went to get another package of ear tubes to replace the ones that had been dropped on the floor. As I entered the OR, I thought it would be funny to come in like a Ninja warrior with the small package of ear tubes in my hand.

Taking large steps and waving my arms in slow motion Ninja-style, I approached the surg-tech, and she thought it was very funny. Then, I felt cold disapproval behind me, and turned in horror, to find Dr. R. leaning up against the wall! He must have entered the room while I was gone for the one minute it took me to get the new set of ear tubes! He never said a word, but it was if he had just scored major points proving that I was indeed, an idiot. Now, the surg-tech was really getting into it, and was pretending she was a Ninja also! I tried telling her with my face to quit playing around, but it was to no avail. It still is pretty hilarious to think about it now!

As the months went by and I worked with Dr. R. frequently, we were sometimes put in emergent situations, where we both finally came to admire each other's skills, and became good friends. I love to work his block now, and I like to think that he thinks highly of me as well.

I have lots of Dr. R. stories because of all the hours I have worked with him. A few years back, a new position was created at the hospital for a child life specialist. The job of the child life specialist was to play with, and educate the children before their operation, to reduce their anxiety and help them become familiar with the process. This is a great thing for both the child, their family, and the OR staff. Unfortunately, our first child life specialist was never oriented very well to the surgery area, and so she came onto the scene like a famous toreador comes into the bull ring. She was young, single, and right out of college. She also thought very highly of the college she had attended, and was always announcing to the staff what college she had attended, in an effort to impress us. In her over-confidence of herself, she also assumed that her role as child life specialist took priority over everyone else's job, including the surgeon's! Since she was never formally introduced to us, I wasn't completely sure what her background was, but I assumed that she was not a nurse. One day, when bringing my patient into the OR, she got on the opposite side of the OR table, and asked my patient to move over from the stretcher the patient was on, to the OR table. Now what she didn't know, was that in the recent past a secretary working in the OR had been asked to help move a patient, and the patient had fallen to the floor because the secretary did not really know what she was doing. I also had previously seen this same child life specialist volunteer to perform all kinds of tasks in the OR, like prepping a leg, which she was not qualified to do.

Since the RN circulating the OR is responsible for the patient's safety, I quickly told the child life specialist not to assist me in having my patient move to the OR table. I went on to tell her that we needed to have a talk after the surgery, so that we could clear up what our different roles were in the OR. She became very upset, and ran out of the room, which I thought was strange.

The anesthesiologist that day was a good looking, nice young man who had recently become single, and the only thing I could imagine later, was that she liked him, and was embarrassed that I had corrected her in front of him. I doubt that he was even paying any attention to the whole situation.

After the case was finished, my boss called me, and said that the child life specialist was very upset. A meeting was called to include me, the child life specialist, her boss and my boss, to discuss what had happened. Oh, brother! At the meeting the child life specialist stated that she 'had never been yelled at like that in all her life.' This amazed me, because I hadn't even yelled at her! I felt sorry for her a little, as her boss was a peer of mine that I used to work with on the medical-surgical floor, and who knew me well! The girl went on and on about her college education, and about the famous college she had attended. I asked her if she was a nurse. She denied being a registered nurse. I told her that there were certain tasks that were out of the scope of her practice, and that there were certain roles and tasks that she could not perform. I also told her about my background, which included years of experience working with children. The meeting ended well.

Another time, the same child life specialist had given the patient a toy to play with that consisted of a handle with a top on it that made beautiful colors whirl around. It was the coolest toy, but when you as a circulator, and the anesthesiologist were bending over that patient as the patient was being anesthetized, you didn't want that particular toy thrust into your face. I explained to the child life specialist why we didn't want that particular toy present at induction, but she disregarded me completely. The anesthesiologist, without the child life specialist present, quickly named the toy the 'retinal probe,' meaning it would poke out our eyes, which I thought was very funny!

One morning, Dr R. walked into the holding room to talk with his next patient and the parents, and the child life specialist was there talking with the child, and letting the child play with the mask used for anesthesia, as well as other equipment. Instead of letting the surgeon have priority to talk with the family, the child life specialist continued on, ignoring him, and interacting with the patient and his family. As one can imagine, this did not go over well with Dr. R! Dr. R. asked me later what I thought of the child life specialist, and I told him about my several encounters with her. That did it for him, and he banned her from interacting with any of his patients, which was too bad, because it is a wonderful service. Soon after, that child life specialist fell in love, and quit her job to move abroad. The two women who have gone on to fill her position have worked wonderfully with the children and the OR staff with no problems whatsoever.

Back in two-thousand-and-six, we had a nursing staff

shortage in the OR, so someone in management got the bright idea of importing nurses from the Philippines, who had OR experience. Our managers announced that the nurses spoke perfect English, and that they already had worked in the OR, so they would be the perfect solution for our nursing shortage. They asked us as staff, if we would volunteer to be their 'pen pals,' and write to them before they came over to the United States. I don't think anyone took them up on that, as we saw them as competing for our job, not becoming our 'pals.' I can't remember exactly how many nurses did come over from the Philippines, but it was around eight or ten.

When they did arrive, the nurses did speak perfect English; the only problem was that the average American does not speak perfect English! Before working with those nurses, I had never been aware of just how much slang Americans do use in their speech every day! 'I felt like the pits,' or 'It's a bummer,' are just a few examples of slang commonly used. The Filipino nurses were at a complete loss as to what the patient was talking about! In the OR, we had just had a new computer installed with technology which allowed you to ask it to turn on the overhead lights, and do other various verbal commands. We never ended up using any of it because it wasn't practical, but one witty physician wondered out loud to me if the computer could translate English into Filipino for the new nurses he was having to work with! The nurses from the Philippines never did work out in the OR, because of the language barrier along with the fast pace; but some of them went on to work on the adult medical-surgical floor instead, and were excellent nurses. You have to give some credit to the management for the inventive idea they came up with that time!!!

Chapter

8

Yesterday, we were working with Dr. S. doing eye cases. He is famously talented at fixing children's eyes that are crossed which is called 'strabismus.' The scrub-tech thought it would be funny if the next time the surgeon asked us a question, we would answer, 'none of your strabismus!' The tech, myself as circulator, and the anesthesiologist all agreed on the gag. Sure enough, within a few minutes of getting started on the next case, the surgeon asked the scrub-tech a question, and she answered back, "none of your strabismus!" At first, he was taken aback and looked a little hurt, until we all burst into laughter, and explained our joke to him. Even after that surgeon had finished his block for the day and had left the hospital, if I saw the same scrub-tech in the hospital, and if she asked me a question, I would reply back, "none of your strabismus," and we would laugh and laugh! As I have said, the camaraderie among staff, is one of the most fun things about working in the OR.

I went into the holding room to interview a mom, whose baby was having a bilateral myringotomy with tube placement, commonly known as ear tubes. Just as I was about to take the baby back, I was told by one of the admitting nurses that we needed to draw blood on this twenty-two-month-old baby, and she then handed me a sack holding ten empty blood tubes in it! I asked the mother if she knew that the baby needed to have blood drawn for labs while the baby was here for the ear tube placement.

The mother confirmed the baby's need for bloodwork needing to be drawn. She stated that the baby had seen an endocrinologist last week, and that they had been unable to obtain blood, so she thought that we could draw it in the OR. Ten tubes was almost enough to push me over the edge with my frustration over blood draws, and all the things that can go wrong with them; not to mention, that a similar situation like this had occurred to me just the week before.

As a nurse, you would really like to help the patient and their family by being able to accomplish the blood draw for them. Unfortunately, many times it is a very difficult task to achieve acquiring the amount of blood that is needed. Sometimes, it can be almost impossible to find a vein on very young children in which to place the IV catheter, especially when they are around twelve months old, as many of them are covered in so much baby fat. If you cannot visualize a vein, you have to just insert your catheter where a vein should anatomically be, and hope that you get lucky and hit it. You also have to judge how deeply to insert the IV catheter to find the vein depending on how much baby fat is covering it!

Once an IV is established, it can be very hard to draw several milliliters of blood from a small baby. Their veins are very tiny, and so the size of the IV catheter that you can place in their veins is very small as well.

The next complication is that there are numerous different tubes in which to place the blood. Each tube needs a different amount of blood placed in it, as well as each tube has a different preservative inside which allows the blood to be preserved for that particular test. In the past, I have drawn blood, sent it down in a green tube, only to find out it was the wrong green tube! I had used the light green tube, and I should have used the dark green tube! Also, some blood must be drawn very quickly and placed into the appropriate tube or the blood will become hemolyzed, and be unable to use for the test. Unfortunately, drawing blood out of a tiny baby, and quickly obtaining enough blood for the test do not go hand in hand--another stressor!

A nurse I was working with that day decided to take the bag of tubes back to the pre-surgery nurses, and make them sort out what exactly we needed. It just happened that another nurse I was working with that day in the OR had worked at an urgent care clinic previously, and she was well versed in blood draws, including which tube you needed for various tests. I walked down to pre-surg to retrieve the bag of tubes, and there were three nurses all working on identifying all of the blood tubes. When I asked for the tubes back, they refused, which added to my already great frustration! I stated that maybe we wouldn't be able to perform the blood draw at this time, since it was holding up the other surgeries, and all three of the pre-surg nurses chimed in with one chorus of how easy it was to draw blood on a baby while it was asleep in surgery, versus drawing blood on a baby that was awake.

Now, in theory that is true. However, all of those nurses did not have any idea what I was up against, as far as drawing that much blood, and putting it in the correct container. Rarely, if ever, did any of those nurses ever draw blood for labs. They also were frequently given the order by the anesthesiologist to start an IV on patients over the age of twelve years, before the patients came back for their surgeries, and those same nurses usually didn't start the patient's IV, stating that they didn't have the time, or know how to. I felt like I had gone back in time dealing with one of my teenage children where they were telling me all about something that in reality, they had no clue about! I opened my mouth to reply to the pre-surgery nurses, thought the better of it, shut my mouth, and turned around and walked back to the OR suite.

There, in the OR, a discussion ensued about whether we should proceed with the next patient, since we were still hung up on this one. Special ear tubes had already been opened for this patient, and I didn't want to have to waste any supplies. If we went on to the next patient, we would have to throw out all the supplies we had opened for this case. I just wanted to get this case over with, even if it meant we had a delay for a while getting our blood tubes back. I was so frustrated at this point, that the surgeon, who usually would be the one getting frustrated, was totally mellow about the situation! We had worked together for so many years, that he knew I was about to reach the end of my rope, so he stayed calm, instead of me!

Finally, we were given back our bag of blood tubes and could get on with the case. I placed an IV catheter in the baby after the baby was asleep, and we began to draw blood out with a syringe. Soon, the blood stopped coming, but the anesthesiologist showed me a new trick. If you gently manipulate the IV catheter from side to side you will find a sweet spot where the blood will just flow into your syringe! How I wish I had known that trick in the past! We were finally able to obtain enough blood to fill all the tubes. Hurray!!!!

Down the hall from the OR suites is the recovery room, where patients are taken to recover after their surgeries. A recovery room nurse came flying out of the recovery room stating that she needed help right away with our last patient. I grabbed the anesthesiologist who was talking to our next patient, and we ran into the recovery room. The sixteen-year-old boy had just had his tonsils and adenoids out, and was experiencing a laryngospasm. This happens when your airway physically closes down, and you can no longer get any air into your lungs. Obviously, this is an emergency. This boy had stated earlier that he had been smoking since the age of thirteen! Smoking is bad news. If you are a smoker, your airway is more irritated already from smoking, which can contribute to laryngospasm. Also, having your tonsils out produces some bloody drainage which also irritates your airway. The two circumstances together were the perfect combination for producing this patient's laryngospasm. The anesthesiologist quickly applied positive pressure via a mask and a bag filled with oxygen. I ran to get our succinylcholine out of the medicine drawers in the OR, plus a syringe and a needle to draw it up with.

Succinylcholine is a short-term paralytic, that when given in the IV, acts within seconds to break the laryngospasm. It does last for a while, so the anesthesiologists only give it if it is absolutely required, because the patient will have to be closely monitored afterwards. In this case, the anesthesiologist had me get the succinylcholine ready to give, but hold off on giving it, while he kept up the positive pressure on the boy's airway. At the same time, we were suctioning the patient to see if we couldn't reduce the amount of bloody drainage in the back of his throat.

Finally, his airway began to relax, and his oxygen saturations began to improve. All patients are monitored for oxygen saturation and not only is a number given on the monitor screen, but an audible sound is given off as well. A good oxygen saturation has a high-pitched sound and a low oxygen saturation has a very deep sound, with the pitch rising as the oxygen content improves. This patient's sound went from a deep base to a higher and higher pitch. The patient's coloring also went from blue to pink! The boy received multiple lectures about the evils of smoking that day. Let's hope that the information truly sank in and was heeded!

One afternoon, I was working with Dr. M., who was a pediatric general surgeon. She belonged to a group of pediatric general surgeons, and as one can imagine, they all had very different personalities. Dr. M. was tall, thin, and somewhat high-strung. She was the only female surgeon in the group. Dr. C. was an older, somewhat crusty man who was very experienced. Dr. H. was younger, and pleasant to work with, unless he became stressed. All three surgeons were highly skilled, and very competent.

That day, Dr. M. and I had done a few surgeries together in her block. As we moved on to another case, the phone in our OR suite rang. It was Dr. C., one of her partners. He informed me that the incision on a previous case had dehisced. This meant that the surface incisions had come undone, and that the child would need to be taken back to surgery to have this repaired.

While I was talking to Dr. C., Dr. M. who was eaves-dropping while performing the current surgery, kept asking me what Dr. C. was saying. Now, my first loyalty is to my patient on the OR table. Dr. M. obviously can't do anything at the moment to help the child with a wound that has dehisced, when she is in the middle of another surgery, can she? I kept wondering why Dr. C. didn't just repair the child's wound himself, instead of calling us. Dr. C. told me to inform Dr. M. of the child's wound becoming dehisced.

I knew that if I gave Dr. M. that information, that it would just upset her and make her more nervous, which wouldn't be helpful to my current patient. I told Dr. C. I wasn't going to tell Dr. M. until after my child's operation was completed. Dr. C. couldn't believe that I was not going to follow his dictate! Dr. C. became more forceful over the phone, and insisted that I tell Dr. M.. I insisted that I wasn't going to tell her! Finally, I told Dr. C. goodbye, and hung up the phone. Dr. M. asked me again what Dr. C. had been saying. I told her that I would give her the information at the end of the case, which I did. As the circulator, you need to do what is best for your patient.

Keeping surgical instruments that have been opened for an upcoming case sterile, is obviously very important inside the OR. Once opened, the sterile field which includes instruments and drapes, along with other items needed for the surgery, would be constantly monitored by a staff member. Occasionally, a fly would be spotted inside an OR room, or nearby in the vicinity of the OR rooms. Staff from the OR would quickly spring into action to find, and quickly remove the offending insect. The method of removal was this: an adhesive spray that was used occasionally in the OR was sprayed onto the flying insect. With its wings now covered in sticky spray, the fly would drop like a stone to the floor, and the staff could then quickly dispatch it. If the sterile field was ever contaminated, the entire set-up would have to be broken down and completely replaced.

I sometimes wondered what the manufacturer of the adhesive spray would think about our use of their product in eliminating a fly from the OR!

In the OR room next to where the anesthesiologist sits, is a metal cabinet that has many drawers. On top of the drawers is a computer screen and keyboard. Access to the drawers can be gained by either logging in a private number and password on the keyboard, or by logging in the private number and using a fingerprint login device. Inside the drawers, are a myriad of drugs which the anesthesiologist uses to manipulate all of the patient's bodily functions, as well as supplies used for intubating the patient. Included are rescue drugs like succinylcholine and atropine. Mounted on one side of the cabinet is a small rectangular clear plastic box which also contains emergency drugs. It is there for emergencies when you don't feel that you have the time to go through entering numbers and passwords on the keyboard to access the drawers. The box's side is closed by a plastic tie which has to be broken to gain access. The tricky part is the plastic box hangs slightly down at an angle toward the floor, so the first time I used the box in an emergency, I broke the plastic tie with my fingers, only to have all of the drugs fall to the floor! Most of the drugs come in small glass vials, and one of the vials shattered when it hit the floor! Fortunately, it wasn't the drug I needed, but I made a mental note to always cut the tie with my scissors that I carry, so that I can use one hand to hold the box's side, keeping the drugs from falling to the floor!

Many times, when I start the patient's IV in Dr. R.'s block, if I decide to use the patient's right hand, I will have Dr. R. act as my tourniquet by having him circumferentially apply pressure around the patient's wrist with his hand. Dr. R. sits on the right side of the patient while waiting for me to start the IV, so he is already sitting there. Having Dr. R. act as the tourniquet saves an extra step, and we are always about streamlining anything we can in the OR! I like to put the tourniquet on at the last minute before I start the IV, as I feel it works best that way. Dr. R., like most surgeons, is for anything that hastens him being able to start to perform the surgery. Many times, it is difficult to start an IV on a small child. One-year-olds are the worst, as they are many times covered in baby fat, and you cannot even see a vein! Then, you just have to try and start an IV by inserting an IV catheter where the vein should be. Dr. R. appreciates that I can almost always start the IV with one try, which means no delay in his cases.

Dr. R. usually has a headlight on for his tonsillectomy cases, and since I don't want a light on my IV site, I have trained him to look down or away, when he helps me by performing the tourniquet task. One day, as Dr. R. was performing this task for me, the anesthesiologist made some comment to Dr. R. about how I was so particular over what I wanted Dr. R. to do in helping me. Dr. R., who is very witty, replied, "I would wear a Grateful Dead Bandana on my head, if she wanted me to!" I thought that was really funny. Surgeons want more than anything to be able to start their surgeries with minimal delay.

A surgeon's dream come true, is a 'flip' room, where two rooms that are fully staffed, are dedicated to that surgeon. That way, all of the interviewing, positioning of the patient, IV being started, etc., for one case are all completed, while the surgeon is in the other room finishing the last case. The surgeon doesn't have to wait very long in between cases, but can alternate between the two rooms, saving him a large amount of time! Sometimes, the hospital would accommodate some of the surgeons with a 'flip' room. They loved it!

Many day surgery operations were so quick, that two nurses were needed to work the block. One nurse was needed to sit at the computer, and electronically record the operation being performed, while the other nurse as the circulator was taking care of the patient. One day, I was working on the computer in the corner of the room for Dr. R.'s block, and a newer nurse was the circulator taking care of the patients. We were having a particularly fun day. Funny quips had been flying all morning, and I was having a good time laughing. Dr. R. joked that I must have a nitrous oxide leak over by where I was sitting. Nitrous oxide is commonly known as laughing gas.

One of our last patients that day was a fifteen-year-old girl coming in to have her tonsils and adenoids out. I always look at the weight recorded in the patient's chart, because some of our teenage patients can be very heavy, and if they are heavy, we are required to put a hover mat on the bed, so we can move them easily after their operation.

A hover mat is like an air mattress, only to begin with, it has no air in it. The deflated mat is placed on the surgery table, and after the surgery is completed, it is then inflated with air, and the hover mat with the patient lying on top of it can be moved onto their stretcher easily, reducing injuries to the staff.

This particular girl only weighed one-hundred-and-forty-one pounds, which did not require a hover mat, but the circulator pointed out that the girl's height that had been recorded on the electronic chart was two-foot-two inches! Now obviously that was a typo, but the thought of a person two-foot-two inches weighing one hundred and forty-one pounds just threw us over the edge. I was laughing so hard that I was crying! When we have fun days like that, I would almost work in the OR for free!

After working in the OR for a couple of years, I really wanted to be taught how to scrub cases. Management agreed, and so I worked alongside experienced scrub-techs while they assisted the surgeon with their cases.

The scrub's duties include making sure that the relevant instruments are available for each case, and also to ensure that the instruments are, and continue to be, sterile. All instrument pans come with sterile indicators that turn a certain color after being correctly processed, which ensures that those instruments are sterile.

The scrub sets up the sterile field, and places the instruments most likely to be used by the surgeon on a mayo stand. The mayo stand is a stainless-steel tray that can be placed over the OR bed during the surgery. It stands on an adjustable pole, so the height of the mayo stand can be changed if needed. This way, the scrub can quickly hand the surgeon the instruments they need. The scrub also can assist the surgeon by holding retractors to hold the incision open.

In all cases, the scrub person is responsible for keeping track of any sharps, such as knife blades, bovie tips, suture needles, hypodermic needles, etc. Bovie tips are the tips placed on the end of cautery handpieces. They come in many forms: sharp needle tip, curved, insulated at the end of the tip, etc. The scrub person is responsible for handing off to the circulator any specimens or cultures that are obtained during the surgery. At the beginning and end of any large case, where it would be possible for the patient to retain any of the following items, the scrub must count all of the instruments, sponges, and sharps with the circulator. The beginning count and the ending count must match!

I enjoyed very much learning how to scrub the small cases that came through the day surgery area. It made me a better circulator as well, because I was more aware of what was needed for all of the various surgeries.

Chapter

9

One day, I was doing a block of urology cases with Dr G..
He is witty and handsome, but his most wonderful attribute is
that he is extremely nice. Everyone loves working with him,
because the atmosphere in his room is so wonderful. Most of
the cases he performs are day surgery types of cases, but he
also performs big cases like nephrectomies, where a kidney is
removed because of disease. He also does ureteral reimplants
fairly often. Your kidney has a tube of tissue on it called a
ureter that drains urine made in the kidney into the bladder. If
that tube or ureter is not attached at the correct spot on your
bladder, you can get infections which can ultimately damage,
and even destroy your kidney. Dr. G. detaches the ureter and
places it in the correct spot on the bladder, so that the kidney
can drain properly. Sometimes, the ureter itself is malformed,
and needs to be surgically altered before it is reattached.

One day, we were doing a simple case with Dr. G. The
PST's (Post-Surgical Technician) job is to stock the
anesthesiologist's cart with supplies that the anesthesiologist
may need before, or during a case. The PST asked the
anesthesiologist Dr. K., if he needed anything in any of his
drawers to do the case. "No, No, No, I don't need a thing," he
kept insisting. Before I even had a chance to start the IV, Dr K.
tried to intubate the baby. Usually, the anesthesiologist waits
until the patient has an IV before trying to intubate the

patient. That way, if the patient has a laryngospasm while being intubated, rescue drugs can be given intravenously to quickly reverse the laryngospasm.

The baby went into a laryngospasm! As we heard the oxygen saturation pitch go down, down, down, and watched the baby's color change from pink to blue, our stress levels went up, up, up! Dr. K. started asking for supplies he needed. I was able to start an IV, push a resuscitation drug, help Dr. K. get the supplies he needed, and the baby pinked up right away. I wasn't going to say a word, but Dr. K. asked me what I thought about the whole situation. Now Dr. K. is a unique anesthesiologist, in that he makes you feel completely comfortable when you are with him. You feel that you can talk to him as if he were your peer--which he is not. He speaks three languages fluently, trained in medical school first as a urologist, and then went through more years of training to become an anesthesiologist!

So I told Dr. K. what I thought. "Are you crazy? You knew I didn't have an IV in yet, and you kept telling everyone, no, no, no, I don't need anything for this case." Dr. G., the surgeon, smiled and told me, "The thing I like most about you is that you never hold back on saying what you think." Dr. K. has since often brought up that situation after seeing me walking down the hallway, and repeats to me 'are you crazy?' as a playful reminder of that day!

Being on-call is the bane of most surgeons, nurses, and scrub technicians that work in the OR. One positive for working in the OR is that you usually are not scheduled to work any weekends, unlike working on the med-surg floor, where you are required to work every other weekend. The downside of working in the OR for me was that I was on-call at least one night a week, and on-call for the entire weekend every four to six weeks. The management would like me to arrive at the hospital in about twenty minutes after being called in if possible, but I live thirty minutes away. Because of that, I need to leave my house right away when the call comes.

Call usually started after the day shift was over, and you could be called into work at any hour of the evening or night. I have been called in to work while I am in the shower, and have my head fully soaped up with shampoo! Many times, I have been awakened in the middle of the night by an unrecognizable noise, that finally turned out to be the telephone ringing next to my bed, with someone on the phone from the hospital asking me to come in! Some OR nurses live too far out to be able to drive in quickly when called in, so when they are scheduled to be on-call, they have to come into town, and sleep in a sleepover room in the hospital! I think it would be nice if there was a hospital policy that anyone over the age of sixty years old didn't have to take call, but that is not how it works.

Small and petite, she was about twenty years old, and stated that she was a college student. When she talked, she sounded like she had something stuck in the back of her throat. It was her enlarged tonsils. Having repeated bouts of tonsillitis, her roommates in college were at their wits end from the bad smells emanating from her mouth, and listening to her loud snoring.

Most children are terrified of the prospect of having to come to the operating room to have their tonsils removed, but this young lady was very excited to have her tonsils out, once and for all enabling her to get on with her life. There are several ways to remove tonsils. Most involve cautery of some kind. One method is with a harmonic scalpel, which in actuality is not a scalpel at all, but a handpiece that uses ultrasonic technology to cauterize and cut the tissue at the same time. This technology became available around two-thousand and five. Another more old-fashioned method for tonsil removal is where the surgeon separates the tissue surrounding the tonsil with a knife and scissors. Then, with a Tenaculum clamp, the surgeon grasps the tonsil and slides a guillotine-like snare over the tonsil. Squeezing the handle, the tonsils are cut from the back of the throat. The cut area is packed with round cotton sponges, until both tonsils are removed, and then the tonsil bed is cauterized, until all the bleeding has stopped. These cotton sponges are the only items necessary to count with this operation, and it is up to the circulator and scrub-tech to ensure that the same number of sponges you started with are present at the completion of the surgery.

There is a saying that if you have your tonsils removed as a child you will never remember it, but if you have them removed as an adult, you will never forget! I think there is a lot of truth to that saying. The college student's removed tonsils were huge, nasty, and scarred from repeated infections, and we could see how much trouble they had given her. Once the surgery was completed, the anesthesiologist and I took her back to recovery, and continued on with our list of surgeries for that day--known as a 'block.' Both the anesthesiologist and I felt sorry for our patient, knowing that it would probably be a somewhat difficult time for her when she awakened. Even with pain medication, some operations are rougher than others to recover from. After taking our next patient to recovery, we saw our first patient, the college girl, being wheeled out of the recovery room. Sitting up, and with a huge smile on her face, she waved to both of us like a beauty queen as she went by. Both the anesthesiologist and I looked incredulously at each other. She was the happiest post-tonsillectomy patient that I have ever witnessed!

One thing that has always annoyed me greatly in my nursing career is the good nurse vs. bad nurse routine. This situation happened occasionally on the med-surg floor when some nurses did not enforce hospital policies in order to remain popular with the parents. An example of this was keeping the center emergency panel containing oxygen and suction clear of balloons, high chairs, etc. Many nurses did not demand that the panel be kept clear, as the hospital rooms were not spacious, and parents liked keeping items there by the panel. Then, I would come along at the beginning of my shift, and ask that the area in front of the panel be cleared. Most parents were more than willing to move their items, but occasionally a parent would become angry with me, thinking I was just trying to throw my weight around, since the other nurses had never made the same request.

In the OR, the same phenomenon happened more frequently. There, the staff liked to go along with the surgeon or anesthesiologist, so they could be well-liked, and be 'one of the gang.'

In one surgical case I was scrubbing; the surgeon complained at the end of the case of feeling ill, and being nauseous and dehydrated. Since we were in a well-stocked OR, along with the fact that we treat sickness all day as a profession, the anesthesiologist and the circulator sprang into action. The circulator strung together some IV fluid, while the anesthesiologist started an IV on the surgeon. As staff, we had been repeatedly warned about not practicing medicine on each other. Management had instructed us that sick employees needed to go to the ER for treatment.

I warned the circulator that if our nurse manager happened to come into our OR room, and witnessed what was going on, we would all be in big trouble. The circulator looked directly at me and asked, "Are you going to squeal on us?" "No, but that still doesn't change the fact that we are not following hospital policy," I replied.

Obviously, if the circulator had insisted that the surgeon had to go down to the ER to receive treatment, the surgeon would not like it. This way, by being treated in the OR with fluids and anti-nausea medication, she could recover more quickly and carry on, not to mention that no bill would be generated that she would have to pay.

I wanted to be liked by physicians as much an anyone, however, I did feel an obligation to my employer to play by the rules. This good nurse vs. bad nurse happened in many other situations as well, and I always found it very frustrating.

One time, a surgeon confided to me that one of his past patients had been a teenage immigrant boy, that didn't have a legal guardian here in this country. The surgeon, in an effort to help the boy, had knowingly admitted, and done surgery on the boy, having someone else pretend to be the boy's guardian. The boy got his surgery, and all turned out well. My problem with that situation was that while the surgeon had decided to take on the extra liability in case anything had gone wrong, and the true guardians had decided to sue; the hospital, which would have also been involved in the lawsuit, didn't have the same opportunity of deciding if they wanted to take on that extra liability as well.

Every year we treated hundreds of children in the OR, whose teeth had been rotted by decay. 'Bottle mouth' is caused by giving young children a bottle of milk or juice at bedtime. The child sucks on the bottle, falls asleep, and the teeth are coated with milk or juice that pools in their mouth. Bacteria thrive all night on the milk sugars, which over time destroys their teeth. I have seen many children whose front teeth were decayed to the point where nothing was left, but the root and a tiny brown nubbin of tooth!

To repair the patient's teeth, the child would be given a general anesthetic, and the dentist could then perform the dental work necessary to correct all the decay. This would often include removing many of the child's baby teeth.

To prevent bottle mouth, only water in bottles should be given at bedtime. Parents will tell you that the child doesn't want water in their bottle, but sometimes as a parent you have to take a stand, and do what is best for your child, whether they like it or not. Rotting teeth actually kills some children every year! The tooth becomes severely decayed and then abscessed, allowing bacteria to enter the child's bloodstream. The child can then become septic and die, if left untreated! What a terrible tragedy to die from a completely preventable and treatable condition!

Yesterday, I was called in to do a case involving a premature baby that had been born after thirty-five weeks of gestation. Normal gestation for babies is forty weeks, and babies born early are referred to by their age in gestational weeks. A twenty-four weeker, is about the limit for survival, which is really amazing, as that is only about half of the time it takes for a normal, full-term baby to develop. My case, was a baby that was only five weeks early, but who had been born with gastroschisis. This is a condition where there is a defective hole in the infant's abdomen in-utero, and some of the intestines develop outside of the abdomen. When the baby is born, the intestines cannot be put back into the abdomen right away, because the abdomen didn't develop in-utero to be large enough to hold them. The solution to this defect, is that the intestines are put in a 'silo,' which is a clear plastic bag that holds the intestines together protecting them from infection, and channels them back into the abdomen. By hanging the top of the silo bag up from a bar over the infant's crib, and with the baby laying on its back, gravity encourages the intestines to move down into the abdomen, and gives the abdomen time to become large enough to hold the intestines. After a few weeks, the intestines can be put back surgically into the abdomen, and the hole in the abdomen is closed completely.

This baby was a darling little boy, with lots of beautiful hair! He had already had his silo bag placed a few days earlier, but because he had developed a fever, the surgeon wondered if he was developing an infection. He was brought back to the OR for cultures to be taken, for the intestines to be cleaned, and for a new silo bag to be put on. This was a perfect case of how wonderful modern medicine is; in that this baby can expect a completely normal life after this defect is corrected, and yet a few decades ago this baby would have perished.

Working with the various staff in the OR was wonderful. Many hours are shared by the staff during long operations, or in the case of day surgery, large blocks of surgeries keep the same staff members together for many hours.

Speaking of wonderful staff, Kate is a middle-aged woman of African American and American Indian descent. She has a heart of gold, is a very hard worker, and is funny to boot! She has all kinds of funny expressions of language. If someone is rude or annoying, she calls them 'dodo birds,' or 'monsters.' To emphasize a point, she will add 'for real' on the end of her sentence. If someone is talking crazy, she will say 'they are talking cray-cray to me,' or 'they are cray to the eighth power.' If she is being overworked, she will say 'they worked me like I was a twin.' If the surgeon is being too complicated in their use of instruments, she will say they are being too deep, or 'deepilicious.'

Someone once asked Kate if she ever went snowboarding. She said "No!" with all of the attitude she could muster. She said, "I am forty-thirteen, and my people don't snowboard." I asked, "what does forty-thirteen mean?" She explained that it was her age, which was fifty-three. Clever! What do you mean 'your people' don't snowboard, I asked? She explained that African Americans in general do not go snowboarding. She said, "we hate the cold, and it is something we just don't do."

She thinks that I live way too far out of town, and when I invite her over to my home, she will say that I live out in 'the cuts.' In the morning, she greets us with 'Hi chicksters!' She calls the heart team, 'the princess squad.' She works as a surgical technician, and is great to work with because she is so experienced, and helpful. She will do anything to help get the case going. I love working with her.

The OR is the only area in the hospital I can think of, that has extra staff to replace you when you go on breaks and lunches. On the med-surg floor where I worked before, when you went on a break, there was no one to replace you, so your work just got further behind! For that reason, I would usually skip my fifteen-minute breaks, and just take my lunch break. When I came to work in the OR, I was amazed to see the extra staff coming in your room to replace you, while you took your breaks, and lunch.

This last week, I went into a room to give the circulating nurse a break, and I noticed that the surgeon who was an ENT (Ear, Nose, and Throat) surgeon was using only a headlight on his head to operate by. ENTs love using a headlight. A headband goes around their head and a spotlight is on the front of it. The spotlight is adjustable, and the power of the light can be adjusted on the newer ones as well.

This particular surgeon had his headlight on low, and was operating on the patient's mouth and jaw. The operative field seemed awfully dark to me. I asked the surgeon if he wouldn't like the big overhead lights turned on, and he said 'yes.' I turned both of the overhead lights on, and the operative field was suddenly flooded with light! Next, the surgeon asked me how high his headlight was turned on. It was on the lowest setting, so I turned it to high. The difference was literally like night and day! The surgeon said nothing further, but I marveled that neither he nor the scrub-tech, noticed that they were working in the dark! The anesthesiologist who stays up by the head of the patient during the case, was an ex-military man. Whenever I see him in the hallway, I give him the army 'who-wah' just for kicks. After I fixed the lights, he couldn't wait to scramble to the back of the room where I was sitting, and tell me that the nurse I was replacing needed to be 'put on report.' At first, I didn't understand what he was talking about but then I understood that it was his way of joking about the light incident, and that the previous circulator should have caught the fact that the surgeon was operating in the dark.

Another circulator was going to start a big belly case. This meant that all the instruments needed to be counted, and so she asked me if I could help her by doing that, so she could go interview and bring back the patient. I counted the instruments along with the surgical-tech, who was going to be doing the case. Afterwards, I went on my way and was in the break room taking my afternoon break, when an overhead page asked me to return to the room where I had counted the instruments a short while ago. Upon entering the room, the circulator asked me if I had counted like she had asked me to. I said I had. She sternly asked me how would she know that, since I had not put my initials up on the board which we usually do, but since the surgical-tech was the same person I had counted with, I assumed that the surgical-tech would just tell her it was me, plus the circulator already knew it was me, because she was the person who had asked me to count in the first place!

I told the circulator that the surgical-tech knew it was me, but that I would be happy to put my initials up on the board for her. Then, everyone in the room burst out in laughter, as they were just jerking my chain for entertainment's purpose! The poor surgeon, who had just entered the room during all of this, was the only one besides me, who was in the dark. Dr. S., the anesthesiologist, was laughing the hardest, which he is rarely seen doing. That tickled me, and I told the group that I was happy to have provided them with their afternoon entertainment! The main fun of working in the OR is that the staff likes to make work fun, as well as give great patient care.

Chapter

10

An orchiopexy was a common procedure performed by our urologist. In the womb, a baby boy's testicles form in the abdomen and as they develop, they are supposed to move down a channel into the scrotum. Sometimes things don't go as planned, and one testicle can remain in the abdomen. If allowed to stay there, the undescended testicle has a higher incidence of developing cancer, and so it was not unusual for the surgeon to perform several orchiopexy cases a week.

First, an incision is made in the lower abdomen over the area where the undescended testicle is, and after locating the testicle, the surgeon spends a fair amount of time dissecting the tissue surrounding the testicle, so that he can get enough length on the spermatic cord enabling him to bring the testicle down to the scrotum.

Another incision is made in the corresponding side of the scrotum, and the surgeon then places a long clamp through the incision in the scrotum up into the lower abdomen. The edge of the testicle is secured with the clamp, and then brought down into the scrotum. The testicle is sutured in place in the scrotum, and then the scrotal incision and abdominal wound are both sutured closed.

He was old enough to know better. The boy was thirteen years old, and was out of control in the pre-surgery holding room. He was scheduled to have an orchiopexy. Totally uncooperative, he wouldn't change from his street clothes into the hospital gown provided to him, or take the sedative ordered by the anesthesiologist! His parents were pleading with him to cooperate, but he was obviously the one in control in their family. I had a new nurse resident with me that was learning the ropes of the OR, and so I was letting her do the interviewing and explaining to the parents. This was a difficult situation. Sometimes, you can talk too much when a patient is distressed, and sometimes it is just better if you take them back to the OR, and get going. At a certain point talking no longer has any beneficial purpose.

He was big for thirteen, and as I saw it, we had two options. We could take him back with him out of control, or we could forcibly hold him down in the pre-surgery room while the anesthesiologist gave him a drug which would incapacitate him. Neither were good solutions. I decided to take over the situation from the resident, and just take the patient back to the OR. Sometimes just separating children from their parents will gain you some control. The boy remained on his stretcher as we went back to the OR. Once we were inside the OR room, we positioned his stretcher next to the OR bed. The boy took the stance of leaning with his back against the raised side rails of his stretcher and spreading his arms out to the sides, grabbing the side rails and bracing himself, so that no one would be able to move him.

Suddenly, the boy vaulted from his stretcher onto the OR bed in an effort to leap across the OR bed, and run away! As he jumped onto the OR bed, the anesthesiologist, who was at the head of the bed, grabbed the boy's upper body, and I leaped onto his middle section. Now I was on the OR bed as well as the boy, but he was very strong, so I was yelling for help at the same time. The surgeon was astonished as he came into the room at about the same time as all of this was going on, and the nurse resident's eyes were as round and big as saucers, as she stood there in astonishment! The anesthesiologist administered gas through a mask and the boy finally lost consciousness. The surgeon asked if the patient would remember this whole scenario, and since he had refused to take his pre-op medicine which included Versed, the answer was yes; he would remember it all, and so would the rest of us! Looking back, I think I would have preferred to have given him medicine forcibly in the holding room, although that would have really stressed out his parents, so it is a hard situation to call.

A similar case involving an out of control teenager was this: a young teenage girl had been brought in by her parents to have an elective surgery. She likewise, had refused to take her pre-op medication, and so was fully awake when I brought her back to the OR room. Once back in the room, the girl refused to get on the OR table, and jumped off the OR stretcher she had been on, and stood defiantly in a corner of the OR. When we tried to talk and reason with her, and get her to cooperate with us, she became combative. The wild teenager stood away from the doors of the OR room, so it didn't really appear that she was going to make a break for it and leave, she just wasn't going to cooperate at all with us when it came to getting on the table, and allowing the operation to take place.

The staff in the room, especially the anesthesiologist, all quickly geared up to physically take her down. As the circulator, I told everyone in the room to stop, and just wait for a few minutes while I went out to talk over the situation with her parents, who were out in the surgical waiting room. My concern was that without any medication on board, the girl would remember us taking her down physically, and it seemed to me to be too close to being an assault! I wanted to make sure that the parents understood the situation we were having with their daughter, and that they both agreed with our use of forcing the girl to have the operation. After talking to both of the parents and explaining the situation, both parents stated that they understood, and gave their consent to physically hold down their daughter so that the operation could proceed.

I returned to the room, where the staff and the uncooperative girl were waiting to find out what the outcome of my conversation with her parents was. "Her parents want us to proceed," I announced to the room, and the girl was placed on the OR table, and firmly held until she fell asleep. I made sure that I documented thoroughly the conversation that I had had with both of her parents, in case there was any trouble over the case later. There never was.

It is not uncommon for children to stick objects in their ears, nose, and I once even met a little girl that put a pink plastic Barbie shoe in her vagina! Today, we fished a rock out of a little girl's ear which was not unusual in itself, but was impressive because of its size, which was the size of a pea! It was so big that the surgeon had a difficult time removing it.

I remember when I worked on the medical surgical floor, I had a patient about twelve years old, that had a stack of coins stuck in his trachea that had to be removed in surgery! He was old enough to know better, and I asked him why he had swallowed all those coins. He stated that he didn't want his sister to get the coins! Wait until his parents get the bill for that procedure!!! We also saw cases fairly frequently that involved young children swallowing tiny round batteries. These could be very dangerous, as the batteries contained acid inside them. If a child swallowed a battery, the battery could adhere to their intestines, leak acid, and perforate their intestinal wall! If caught early, we would go in with a scope through the child's mouth, and see if the battery could be found and removed, before it did any damage. If the parents were unaware that their child had swallowed a battery, and the battery was not removed; it could prove fatal if the acid the batteries contained perforated the child's intestinal wall, allowing intestinal material to leak into the abdomen causing a peritonitis similar to having a ruptured appendix.

It is so important to keep objects like these away from babies and toddlers, which can be difficult to do.

One winter, our area experienced a huge snow and ice storm. I was scheduled to work and because the roads were so bad, I had my husband drive me into work. It took quite a while for him to put chains on the car tires, so I called work to let them know I would be late. Finally, we were underway. The terrain around the hospital is very steep and hilly. My husband started up one hill, and I protested that we would get stuck in the snow. He disagreed, and so up we went.

When we got about half-way up the ice-covered hill, he lost control of the car, and the car skidded to the right, ending up on the curb! My husband told me it would be best if I walked in the snow the rest of the way, which seemed like the best plan to me as well. The hospital was only about a block away.

After helping him shove the car off the curb, I began to trudge through the snow and ice towards the hospital. I finally ended up inside the building's basement, but as the hospital is several stories high, and has multiple wings, I ended up in an area that was totally unfamiliar to me! I found myself walking through abandoned nursing stations, and I thought to myself how funny it would be if I was lost inside the building, and couldn't find my way out!

Usually, when you are late to work, they make you a 'facilitator,' which means you are a helper-bee, and are not a circulator in charge of a 'block,' or group of surgeries. Instead, I found that I had been assigned to be the circulator in a block involving the fastest ENT surgeon we had! I was forty minutes late; and seventeen people had called out, which meant we were incredibly short of help! I had no hope of getting my OR room ready before the surgeries were to begin. Fortunately, Lisa, another RN, had thought to set up my room for me earlier that morning, or I would have really been in a world of hurt! I still was completely overwhelmed because I was also to be the only RN in the room that day. Normally, another RN would be working on the computer, recording the operation, and helping to clean and turn the room over for the next patient. How on earth was I ever going to keep up? I was close to tears, but I knew that if I started to cry, I would really be sunk.

Both the surgeon and the anesthesiologist, noting my distress said, "Just tell us what we can do to help you, and we will do it," which was very sweet of them. Somehow, we managed to get through the day. I might add here, that the patients always seem to show up for their scheduled surgeries in spite of severe weather conditions! I once asked one of the mothers how she had made it in to the hospital with such terrible driving conditions. She told me that they drove in to the hospital the night before, and had stayed at a hotel!

After the block was finished, my nursing director's secretary came up to me, and told me that management had decided that they would not be counting this incident of tardiness against me! I was completely and utterly dumbfounded! I felt that I should have been given an award, plus a free lunch for making the heroic effort I had made to get to work that day, when seventeen other people had decided to stay home and drink hot chocolate! I thought to myself that if they had counted me as tardy that day, I would have never again made the effort to come in on a horrendously snowy day!

In the afternoon, we had a case involving a sixteen-month-old boy that had become hoarse after eating almonds a few days ago. His hoarseness had never resolved, and so today, he was scheduled to have a direct laryngoscopy to see if an almond was lodged somewhere in his bronchioles. After the toddler was anesthetized, a scope was placed down the child's trachea and bronchioles. The scope has a camera piece attached to it so that the image can be seen on overhead monitors hanging from the ceiling. After probing for a few minutes, a white object was seen down one bronchiole. (Your trachea splits into two bronchioles where each bronchiole goes into a lung.) A grasper was placed down the trachea into the bronchiole, and after a few attempts the white object was grasped. While watching the monitor, we all cheered as we watched the surgeon's progress at pulling the almond towards the patient's throat and then out of the child's mouth. On the monitor, the fragment of almond looked huge, but once the almond was laying in front of us, it was only the size of a sunflower seed! Another successful surgery!

I worked on a weekly basis with Dr. S., an ophthalmologist.

He performed several different operations routinely, including removing chalazions, probing blocked tear ducts, along with doing strabismus repairs. Less frequently, he also would remove cataracts from children's eyes.

Today, we did a case involving a chalazion. A chalazion is essentially a pimple on the underneath of the eyelid. Chalazions can occur in both the upper and lower eyelids, and some can get amazingly large. If left untreated, they sometimes rupture on the outside of the eyelid. To perform this operation, the patient is anesthetized with a mask only. No endotracheal tube is needed because the surgery is so quick. The surgeon takes a special clamp that has a large round circular part that encircles the chalazion on the inner part of the eyelid. The back of the clamp is solid metal, and clamps down on the outer part of the eyelid. After placing the clamp, the surgeon then turns the eyelid inside-out to expose the inner part, and makes a small incision with a knife blade into the chalazion. Next, an instrument like a miniature ice cream scoop reams out the pus inside, followed by sterile Q-tips.

As one anesthesiologist stated during this process, "That is so disgusting, and yet so satisfying!" A steroid is injected into the chalazion area to help reduce inflammation, and then some local anesthetic is also injected into the chalazion area to numb the area, so it is not as painful. This operation only takes a matter of a few minutes. Antibiotic and numbing drops are placed in the eye. An eye patch is placed over the eye for a few minutes just to absorb any bleeding that occurs.

One day, we had a cataract removal case, and the phaco machine wasn't cooperating. The phaco machine is a large machine that sits on four wheels, and has a computer screen on the top of it. A large foot pedal is attached to the base of the machine by a cord. The phaco machine has an IV pole built onto the side of it, and the IV pole can be electronically raised up and down. A large bottle of BSS (Balanced Salt Solution) infused with a minute amount of epinephrine which helps to reduce bleeding, is hung on the IV pole and is used to prime the tubing as well as to rinse the eye during the operation. The phaco machine performs all of the functions needed to accomplish the cataract removal operation.

Before the child was even brought back to the OR room, we made sure that the phaco machine was working properly. The computer was turned on, and then given time to go through its several internal checklists. Then, we loaded the tubing into the machine and primed the tubing. The first problem that we encountered was that the tubing failed to prime correctly. The computer screen tells you that the priming has failed, even though physically it appeared that the fluid had gone through the tubing correctly. We repeated the priming twice, with failures both times! While that was happening, the scrub technician was looking at the computer screen while working with a knife blade, and she accidentally stabbed her finger with the blade. The cut was over a quarter of an inch deep, and was actively bleeding. This put her out of the operation, as you can't scrub and keep your field sterile, while you have an actively bleeding puncture wound! It was decided that I would scrub the case until help arrived, as I have scrubbed cataract cases before.

After I scrubbed in, we replaced the tubing, and the third set of tubing finally primed correctly. We were all happy with that, but then the screen on the computer started to oscillate and have black lines jump in and out of the screen, which I had never seen it do in the last decade! I suggested to both the surgeon and the anesthesiologist that the best thing to do might be to cancel the case, have the phaco machine looked at, and reschedule the case for later. The surgeon had me test the pressure of the phaco tip by putting my fingers around the tip to simulate being inside the eye, and then pressing the foot pedal to see if the pressure would build up as it normally should, which it did. The surgeon said that he wanted to proceed with the operation. My biggest fear was that we would be in the middle of the whole operation, and the computer screen would just go black on us, and then we would be in a real pickle!

Fortunately, the case went well, the phaco machine worked as it should, and towards the end of the case both the surgeon and anesthesiologist started joking about how if the phaco machine hadn't worked properly, they both would have said in their report that they wanted to cancel the case, but that I insisted as the circulator that we go forward! They both laughed heartily at their joke, and we were all relieved to have completed a successful case.

Chapter

11

Yesterday I worked with Dr. N., a dentist of middle eastern descent. He had a patient that was a sixty-year-old woman with a history of aortic stenosis, and she needed a heart-valve replacement. Before they would perform her heart operation, the cardiac surgeons wanted her to have some dental work performed, as decaying teeth can become infected, which could compromise her heart-valve replacement. Every year there are cases of people becoming septic from the bacteria in their decaying teeth entering their bloodstream, and then dying of septicemia! I usually only worked on pediatric cases, but occasionally, I would be asked to do a case with an adult, like this one.

Dr. N. extracted one of her teeth, and also cleaned and looked at the rest. This procedure was all done under a local MAC anesthesia, where the patient is not completely asleep during the procedure. With a local MAC, the anesthesiologist gives the patient a light sedative, and monitors the patient throughout the procedure. The dentist also uses a local medication to numb any area that might cause pain.

Because the patient is only sedated, the OR staff in the room need to be somewhat guarded in their conversation during the procedure. The last thing the patient wants to hear is someone being silly in the OR, while they are there having their procedure done.

When I first came to work in the OR in two-thousand and one, I worked with Dr. N. a lot in the children's day surgery area. He has a very fun sense of humor. One time out at the desk area, I was having a crazy conversation with our OR secretary about two different types of people: people that reuse their towels after taking a bath or shower, and those that have to wash their towel after every bath or shower. The conversation came about because I was frustrated at always having to wash towels at my house, because my teenage children wanted to have a fresh towel for every shower! This particular secretary stated that she always needed to have a clean towel as well, and I was discussing the theory that since you have just washed your entire body and are clean, that the towel used could be hung back up to dry and reused, since it should be essentially clean.

Dr. N. overheard the conversation, and jumped in agreeing with me that the towel would still be theoretically clean. He went so far as to question the secretary about the quality of her cleaning all the different parts of her body when she was bathing! His theory was like mine, that the towel would still be clean and could be reused! We were all laughing hard over this conversation. This is a good example of the silly conversations that go on around the OR at various times. I am sure these conversations take place in all work settings, but somehow, I think the public sees us as being 'serious professionals.' We are professionals, but are sometimes anything but serious!

Today, we operated on a little two-year-old girl who had crossed eyes. We usually do about four of these strabismus cases a week. The surgeon cuts the muscle on each side of the eye, and sutures the muscles in a different area on the eyeball, so that the eyes are not crossed anymore. These are cases that can make a student nurse ill, as the surgeon sometimes sticks a Q-tip in the eye for a few minutes to stop any bleeding. As one can imagine, seeing a patient with a Q-tip sticking out of their eye can bother a person, and we have had more than one student nurse that has had to leave the room quickly during this operation!

Very tiny needles attached to suture are used to stitch the eye, and the suture is notorious for sticking to the surgeon's slightly bloody gloves as he tries to put the needles back on the mayo stand when he is finished using them. There is a small magnetized box that the needles and other sharps are placed on during the operation. This magnetized box is supposed to hang on to the needles while the case is in progress, but in this case, the needles are so tiny that they are actually smaller and lighter in weight than the suture that is attached to them, making them very easy to lose. We usually use six needles in each one of these cases, but today the surgeon was going to work on two muscles on each eye, so we had a count of eleven needles. After the first eye was done, we still had the eleven needles, but for the final count after the second eye was done, we only had nine needles, which meant that two needles were missing! The fact that anything is missing drives everyone in the room completely nuts, as we have a hospital policy that an X-ray has to be taken in an effort to find the missing item, and also an incident report has to be filled out if the missing article is never found.

We searched the drapes along with the mayo stand, and finally after several minutes, I managed to find one of the missing needles stuck on the child's head drape. We continued to search and search for the last missing needle, but to no avail. The thing that makes me the craziest is that you know that the needle is there somewhere, but you just don't know where! I brought in a long thin bar of magnetized iron and 'swept' the floor with it in an effort to find the missing needle, but still no luck. The surgeon had confirmed that no needles were in either eye, but since hospital policy is that an X-ray must be taken, we had a portable X-ray done. The radiologist confirmed the same information--no needles remained in either eye.

Another time, I was scrubbing in a belly case, and at the end of the surgery, I couldn't find a tiny clamp which I knew had never even been used in the case! Keep in mind that some instrument sets may contain over eighty instruments! It made me so mad that I couldn't find it, but if you cannot produce it when the final instrument count is done, an Xray has to be taken. After the X-ray was taken, the clamp was located under some other clamps still in the container that the instruments are kept in. Very frustrating!

I saw Dr. M., an anesthesiologist, out by the front control desk looking at the schedule of cases still to be done in the OR. Dr M. worked in the past for the army, and he looks every bit the army man with his big chest and muscular arms. Whenever I see him in the hallway, I give the verbal army 'who-wah' to him as a joke. He teasingly calls me 'per diem,' because after years of working as a staff nurse in the OR, I went 'per diem,' which literally means 'by the day.' Per diem nurses receive no benefits, such as health insurance or vacation pay, but in turn are paid more money per hour, and did not have to take any call, which was the main reason I went per diem. He said to me, "Hey per diem, do you know why I can't get my case to start?" As I was not working with

Dr. M. that day, I had no idea what case he was even talking about. Before I could even answer, he said, "You probably don't know or care why I can't get my case started, right?" My answer: "Sir, yes, sir!" I jokingly replied.

A most interesting case presented itself in the OR. A two-year-old boy came in to be assessed for a urethral defect. In the case of boys, the urethra is a tube that transports urine from the bladder to the tip of the penis. This boy had two openings on the top of the head of his penis, but his true meatus or opening was located close to his anus. This meant that when he urinated, his urine came out close to where he defecated. We were performing a cystoscopy where a scope with a camera was placed in the urethra to view the inside. A cystoscope is an instrument that consists of a long thin straight metal hollow shaft which ends with a larger circular end that has areas of attachment near it called ports. The straight thin end of the scope can end in different angles such as zero degree which means the end is cut completely straight at the end, or thirty degrees, which means it has a thirty-degree angle cut at the end.

Tubing for fluid, which is normal saline or water, is attached to one of the ports near the large circular end. The fluid bathes the urethra, allowing better visualization of the urethra during the procedure. Towards the circular end of the scope is an attachment for the light cord which is attached to a light box by the circulator. Without this light source, the physician would not be able to see anything. The physician can either look directly through the scope with his eye, or a camera can be attached onto the end of the scope. A camera allows everyone in the room to see what the physician is seeing.

Monitors like TV screens hang from the ceiling in the OR. These monitors show the image produced by the scope, and the monitors can be moved in many different positions allowing the physician and scrub technician to see easily. Pictures can be captured as the procedure is done by either the circulator pressing a button on a computer screen located in the back of the room, or the physician can push a button on the camera itself.

During this particular case, the surgeon put the scope up the true urethra which was located by the little boy's rear end. Before the procedure, the surgeon felt that this defect was unrepairable. The uppermost hole located on the top of the penis was completely non-functional, while the lower hole on the head of the penis did seem to have a possibility of being minorly functional. During the procedure the anesthesiologist suggested getting a glide wire to place into the urethra which would allow the surgeon to follow the progress of the wire as it explored these different paths. A glide wire is basically a thin piece of wire used in surgery. When the surgeon put the glide wire in the true urethra at the child's bottom it eventually came out the lower hole of the penis. This excited everyone in the room as the surgeon realized that the defect was repairable, which everyone in the room had been hoping for. Pictures were taken, and a surgery would be scheduled in the future to repair the defect for this little boy.

The OR is unusual in that sometimes there is excess staff in the afternoons when some of the surgery blocks are finished. This never happens in most of the other workplaces in the hospital. Instead of having the extra staff mill around with not much to do, the management will 'low census' some of the staff, which means to send staff home early. To make it fair, the management has devised a system whereby the calls made by staff who call in at five a.m. that day requesting to be low-censused, are taken on a timed basis. In other words, the person who can call in as soon as it turns exactly five a.m. becomes the first person with a chance of going home early, later that same afternoon. If the call is recorded before five a.m., then the staff member's name is not put on the home early list at all!

It is funny to me to think that on any given day, there are at least fifteen staff members who are up before five a.m. just so they can call in to get their name on a list, so they can have a chance of going home early! The staff are unpaid for those hours when they leave early. This system has actually taken on a life of its own! There is great competition among the staff for who can be number one on the list. Even if it is a busy day and no one goes home early, you somehow still feel like you won, if your name was number one on the list that morning!

Yesterday, the charge nurse finally wrote the names up on the white board in the core, of those persons that were allowed to leave and go home early. My name was up on the board, and I was number five on the go-home-early list that day. Also listed, were the number one and two people, who I knew were both in the lounge taking their afternoon break; so I knew that they were both still unaware that they had been excused to leave for the day. I went into the lounge, got my lunch bag, and then stood by the two of them as if I just had to watch one more thing that was on the TV before I left. Lizette, one of the nurses whose name was ahead of mine on the go-home-early list, is incredibly bright and observant. I knew that she would notice me standing there, and fall for the bait. She asked me, "Where do you think you are going?" I told her that

I was going home. She said, "Who told you that you could go home?" I replied that the charge nurse had told me that I could go home, because I was her favorite. As I said this, I gave a wink to a surgical-tech who was a traveler, and didn't know us that well yet. Lizette, the observant nurse, started to become upset that they would let me go home early before her. I started to laugh, and then Lizette knew that she had been had. She gave me guff for fooling around, but she also knew that I had scored by getting her to fall for the gag, so I told her that she had made my afternoon! That morning, I was supposed to have brought Lizette a small butterfly bush from my garden that I wanted to give away, but I had forgotten. Later that afternoon I got a text that simply stated, "butterfly bush--don't forget." This mob-like message cracked me up.

One benefit of working in the OR was that medical scrubs which included a freshly laundered top, pants, and a cover jacket, were provided by the hospital for each employee to wear during their shift. When I worked on the medical-surgical floor, I had to buy my own uniforms, and wash them myself. Working in the OR, I was assigned a locker, and could come to work in my street clothes, and change into fresh scrubs. I did have to purchase my own shoes, which were dedicated to be used only in the OR, and left there until my next shift.

After my shift in the OR was done, I could put my regular street clothes and shoes back on, and go shopping, or visit with friends on my way home. Besides scrubs, a head covering to cover our hair was provided by the hospital as well. Some employees used a homemade fabric cap to cover their hair, but I liked using the disposable head covering that looked like a shower cap, which was provided by the hospital.

The medical scrubs didn't look very stylish, as they came in general sizes, and weren't fitted to the body at all. Once you were dressed in scrubs along with a head covering, the only part of you that showed was your face, which many times was partially covered by a mask.

Even though we worked for many hours with the same surgeons and dentists; many times, those same people would not recognize you when you were dressed in your street clothes with your hair showing, as you passed them in the hospital hallway, or saw them outside of the hospital.

One afternoon, I saw a very nice dentist I frequently worked with, sitting alone in a booth inside the hospital's cafeteria. I had changed into my street clothes, and my hair of course, was now showing. I stopped to say hi to him in a friendly manner, and by his countenance, I could see that he didn't recognize me. Terror filled his face as I began to talk to him, and it took him a minute or two before he finally recognized who I was. A look of relief now filled his face, as he no longer had to worry why some unknown blonde woman had stopped to talk to him! I have to admit I got a kick out of it!

Today, we had a five-year-old patient that had stuck a pink flower-shaped eraser up the right side of her nose! She had tried to retrieve it, but the eraser just kept going up higher and higher into her nose. We commonly removed items out of ears and noses. The first things that parents of small children usually notice is a discharge, along with a foul smell from their child's nose; which alerts them to the possibility that something is not quite right. The most common item we retrieve is usually a rock or bead from their ears, which usually makes the child's ear hurt.

One little girl I had as a patient, had originally come to the OR to have a rock retrieved out of her ear. She had loved the attention, the free toy she had received, along with the popsicles and juice so much, that she kept putting items in her ear, just so she could come back again! When I was her nurse, she was on her third trip back, and her mother was very upset that her daughter kept repeating this behavior! Not to mention what the cost associated with every surgical visit must have been!

When I go in to introduce myself to the parents at the beginning of a case, I ask them if they are the mom and dad. This usually works out fine, but on one occasion as I entered the holding room, and asked the two people there if they were mom and dad, the mom confirmed that she was the mom, but the other person just stared back at me, and didn't say anything. To my great embarrassment, I realized that this was a case where there were two moms and no dad. I told the other person I was sorry, and asked if she was the other mom. Again, the response I got from the unknown person was just a blank stare at me. However, the mom started laughing hysterically, and I realized then that the other person really was the dad after all! There was no way out of this one, so I apologized and vowed never to make any assumptions again! After that incident, instead of assuming they are the parents, I would ask any adults that were in the room with the patient what their relationship was. Years later, to help out the staff, adults were given name tags with their relationship written on the tags, which was most helpful!

Today, we had a case that involved an eleven-month-old baby girl. Her eyes were crossed, and so we were performing a bilateral strabismus repair, where surgery would be done on both eyes to hopefully uncross them. Her paternal grandfather was known to have had malignant hyperthermia, which is a genetic predisposition to not being able to metabolize anesthetic gases normally, and which can result in extreme body temperatures, muscle rigidity, and can end in death if it is not treated in time! Because of the extreme danger, any surgical patient that might be predisposed to having malignant hyperthermia during a surgical case is treated without any anesthetic gases. Special tubing filters are used on the anesthesia machine to ensure that no gases left from a previous case might contaminate the patient.

The patient is put to sleep with an intravenous sedation medication--propofol, which does not cause malignant hyperthermia. Unfortunately for us, this eleven-month-old was covered in baby fat, and was a very difficult IV to start, as no veins could be seen because of her baby fat. Also, because of the potential for malignant hyperthermia we couldn't use anesthesia gas via a mask to put her to sleep before the IV was started, so she was wide awake. I felt so bad when I tried to put the IV in, and the poor baby cried. Fortunately, it only took two tries before I was able to get an IV started successfully, which I was very happy about. Her case proceeded without incident, and her crossed eyes were fixed.

Chapter

12

Yesterday at work, while interviewing the parents of a young boy, I discovered that the boy had eaten some pudding just a few hours before. Unfortunately, we had to cancel his surgery case. The parents stated that they were told in their instructions the night before, that pudding was all right to give to their son. Patients are allowed to have clear liquids up to four hours before their surgery, but any food substance cannot be eaten for about eight hours before surgery. This is because milk and other foods take longer to digest, and therefore, are still in the stomach for many hours after eating them.

If the patient has eaten too close to their surgery time, there is the possibility that the patient may vomit, and then aspirate some of that food into their lungs. If their surgery is an elective procedure the case is cancelled and rescheduled. If the surgery is emergent, then we would have to proceed with the surgery. In an emergent case where the patient has eaten recently, pressure is put on the lower front of their neck by the circulator's fingers during anesthesia induction. This pressure is called cricoid pressure. It prevents any fluids or foods from coming up from the stomach through the esophagus while the anesthesiologist is intubating the patient. Once the endotracheal tube is in place, the tube prevents food from getting into the lungs during the surgery.

Last night, an organ harvest was taking place in the OR on a fifteen-year-old boy who had gotten into his mother's Percocet tablets, and accidentally overdosed. One of the side effects of many drugs including alcohol and narcotics, is respiratory depression. If you take enough of these drugs you will literally quit breathing, and minutes after that, your heart will stop beating from the lack of oxygen, and you will die. That is what had happened to this poor boy. When he was discovered by his parents, he had only been dead for a few minutes, and so some of his organs could still be salvaged.

In organ harvests, the patient is kept on a ventilator at the hospital until the transplant team can be organized and arrive. The patient is brought down to the OR ventilated, and the operation to remove whatever organs are viable proceeds. After the operation, the patient is taken to the morgue, and the transplant team takes the various harvested organs to their destination. What a terrible tragedy for the boy's family, and yet his organs will go on to bless many other people's lives!

The OR crew was doing a block of strabismus repairs where the surgeon was fixing crossed eyes. Dr. S. is an expert at performing these operations, so the staff are usually looking for any form of entertainment during these routine operations, which usually comes in the form of someone accidentally saying something funny. Two circulators are needed to work the eye surgeon's room; one, to perform the patient care, and the other nurse is needed to be on the computer writing the electronic report. Some of the other cases the eye surgeon routinely performs in his morning block only last three minutes, and there is at least eight minutes of solid charting that needs to be done for each case, thus the need for two circulators.

That morning, someone had called my home phone at one-thirty in the morning waking me from a sound sleep. Next, my husband woke me at five-thirty in the morning because my alarm had not gone off. When I checked my alarm, it had been shut off--probably by me, but I had no remembrance of doing it!

At work while doing the block of strabismus repairs, I was feeling very warm, and wondered if I was becoming ill. I looked at the wall register, and the room temperature was seventy-five degrees, but the thermostat was set at sixty degrees. I asked everyone in the OR if they were also hot, and they all now voiced their complaints of how hot they were. I called down to engineering and Cathy, their secretary answered. I told her about the elevated temperature in the OR room, and she said that she would notify the engineers, who were the only ones that had control over the temperature in the old OR rooms. In retelling this information to some of the OR staff, I wasn't completely sure of Cathy's name, and so I said, "Cathy, at least I think," meaning I think her name was Cathy, will look into the heat problem. The other circulator and scrub-tech thought I had said, "Cathy the beast," which would be quite out of character for me to say a thing like that. The staff hooted over this for quite a while.

Next, the anesthesiologist and I were taking a patient down to recovery and he stated, "Only one more case to go." I replied that we still had two more cases. He said, "What do you want to bet that we only have one more case?" By now, we were in recovery with the recovery room nurses present. I complained to him, "what would we bet?" No one is ever really the winner in a bet, as the loser always feels bad. I don't drink alcohol, and I figured he would bet me a beer or something like that, so I told him if I was right, he could get down on his bended knee to me, which I already knew would be the LAST thing he would ever do! He went straight over to a computer to look up our list of patients, and sure enough, we had two more cases! I gracefully let the entire subject drop!

During the last case, the surgeon commented on how pleased he was that all the cases that morning had been finished so quickly. I decided to compliment the surgical-tech student who had been scrubbing with Dr. S. all morning. I stated, "Jeremy is smoking hot," meaning he is really good at keeping up with the surgeon. At this, the OR crew broke into laughter at my blunder. Apparently, what I said did not relate to the student's speed at working, but to how he looked. I was happy to provide them all with some amusement that morning.

It was an unusual case because I was working with an adult patient, and that adult happened to be the mother of my neighbor. The patient was there for back surgery, and my neighbor Kay was there, as well as her sister, to be with their mother before her surgery. During the preop interview questions, Kay's mother denied to the anesthesiologist having had any chest pain recently, having been recently ill, being short of breath, etc., and so we proceeded with the operation.

As soon as we got started with anesthetizing the patient, the anesthesiologist started to complain to me that he was having a difficult time keeping the mother's vital signs stable, which we each thought was weird. As the back surgery progressed, Kay's mother became more and more unstable. So unstable that at one point, we thought we might have to put a sterile towel over her open back wound, and flip her over to start chest compressions! The surgeon was finally able to finish the surgery and Kay's mother was taken to the ICU, instead of to the recovery room. She was not doing well at all. She was put on an external heart pump to try and keep her alive.

I had other surgeries in my block that morning, so I kept working, but wondered all day how Kay's mother was doing. Was she still alive? I frequently called the ICU, and the word there was that they didn't expect her to live! In the afternoon, after my block was finished, I went up to the waiting room still in my scrubs, and sat down with Kay and her family. They didn't seem to grasp the seriousness of the situation, and as I sat down with them, I immediately began to cry. They were astonished to see me crying, and Kay said, "well, that's not good."

Kay's mom did miraculously survive, and after many tests were conducted, it was discovered that she had suffered a heart attack the previous week, that had gone completely untreated! Her family all admitted later, that they all knew that their Mom had been ill the previous week; had been short of breath, etc., and yet they had said nothing while the Mom was being interviewed before surgery, denying all of those symptoms. It really is so important to answer all of the questions truthfully before surgery!

A round, two-inch bruise sits on the front of my left upper leg where I ran into the end of the OR bed yesterday. There are several types of OR tables. The offending table was a standard sixty-five-hundred. The bed weighs several hundred pounds with rollers underneath it, and has four retractable feet. To move the bed, the four feet are electronically retracted up, and then the bed rests on its rollers. Once the feet are down, the bed is immovable! A metal rail runs along both sides of the bed the entire length of the bed. The rail is there so that various devices can be attached to the bed, such as arm boards, leg holders, and mechanical arms, that can hold a retractor during surgery.

These rails stick out past the end of the bed and as you run around the bed you can gouge yourself. I don't know how many times I have been gored by those bed-rails! The sixty-five-hundred bed is used commonly for many different operations, and the head piece can be taken off and put at the foot of the bed to accommodate different surgeries. The bed has a big metal base that is located towards the head of the bed, and if the surgeon needs to sit for a surgery such as an ear case, the bed can be reversed so that the big metal base is under the foot of the bed, enabling the surgeon to put his or her legs under the head of the bed while operating. The top of the table can be swiveled out as well, by turning a handle on the center column which holds the bed up.

Another bed common to the OR is the Cysto table. It is used in urology cases where the surgeon is doing a cystoscopy or other urological surgeries. If radiology is needed to visualize a kidney or ureter, the large cylindrical column on a sixty-five-hundred bed that holds up the bed from the base, would physically be in the way of a C-arm obtaining the X-ray. The Cysto bed is held up by a cylindrical column as well, but the whole top of the bed can electronically slide towards the head, or the feet with a push of a button. This allows the bottom portion of the C-arm which takes the X-ray, to get under the patient's kidneys in a perfect position.

There are many other types of beds used in the OR as well: fracture tables used in orthopedic cases, and Andrew tables, which are used for back surgeries, to name a few.

Yesterday, we had our usual block of surgeries with an ear,

nose and throat surgeon who works every Monday and Wednesday. He always uses a microscope for a lot of his cases, and many of our microscopes are old, and a lot of them have recently needed repairing. When the microscopes are sent out for repair, they never seem to come back. I can only assume that there are no parts to be had anymore for a microscope that is over fifty years old! I had previously talked to management about the fact that the microscopes were all beginning to fail because of their age, and that more ENT surgeons were starting to have regular blocks of surgery at our hospital. It seemed obvious to me that more microscopes needed to be purchased. The answer I got from management was that we didn't have any money in the budget to buy new microscopes.

This morning, when I checked the microscope to make sure that it was in working order before our cases began, the light inside the microscope wouldn't come on. I assumed that it needed a new light bulb, but when I went to put in the new light bulb, I could see that one of the two prongs that held the light bulb in place had broken off inside the socket. That put that microscope out of commission! I found one of our oldest microscopes in our back-equipment room, but it had been sent out for repair recently, and I wasn't too sure how operational it really was. I decided to run across the street to the main hospital, and get a microscope from there to bring over to our day surgery area. Fortunately, they didn't have any other ENT surgeons working that morning; otherwise we may have had to cancel all our cases due to the lack of a working microscope!

The only way to transport the microscope from the main hospital was to push it down the long hallway to an elevator that will go down six floors into a tunnel system that runs under the road located outside the front of the main hospital. After pushing the microscope in the tunnel for a while, the thought occurred to me how strange it would be if I had a heart attack pushing this heavy microscope through these tunnels, and what someone would think coming upon me sprawled out on the floor unconscious next to a microscope!

After finally arriving at the outpatient day surgery facility with the microscope, the ENT surgeon decided he would use the older microscope that I had already brought into the room earlier! During the surgery he had all kinds of problems with that microscope because it didn't work properly, but he persisted on to the end of the cases, and then made the statement that he never wanted to do a surgery with that microscope again. I prepared another work order, and sent that microscope out for repair. I jokingly told Dr R. that one day he would show up for work, and we would just give him a big magnifying glass to work with, instead of a microscope!

We had a new OR nurse resident working with us that day, and early in the morning she became upset, and ran out of the room saying that she was going to go home! She said that she felt overwhelmed, and was upset that she was repeating the same mistakes. She felt that she wasn't progressing as fast as she should. We all felt bad that she had left. Time will tell if she sticks it out and finishes the residency, or if she decides to do something else in the nursing field.

Today, we had a case of a twelve-year-old boy that was scheduled for a right tympanoplasty. This surgery was to repair a hole in his right eardrum resulting from having ventilation tubes placed when he was young, and the hole left by the ear tube in his right ear had never closed up on its own. Most holes caused by placing ventilation tubes in the ears close up on their own, after the ventilation tubes fall out, or are removed by the surgeon. Another nurse had taken care of the patient at the beginning of the case, and so when I arrived to take over after my lunch break, the patient had already been positioned, an IV started, and a warming blanket placed over the top of the patient.

After the operation was completed, I called for moving help to get the patient from the operating table onto the stretcher that he would go to recovery on. The warming blanket has a sticky strip along one edge of it to help keep it in place on the patient. As I pulled the sticky part of the blanket off the patient, I inadvertently pulled his IV out of his left arm! The previous nurse had put the sticky part of the warming blanket right over the top of his IV. I couldn't believe that I had just pulled his IV out! I exclaimed to the anesthesiologist that I had just pulled his IV out, and not seeing the cause of the problem he said, "Why did you do that?" I asked the anesthesiologist to keep the patient asleep for another couple of minutes, and I restarted the IV in his hand. We took the patient to recovery without any further incident.

A case was scheduled to remove viral warts from a child's left eyelid. The anesthesiologist assigned to the case, asked if we had the big respirator hoods to wear over our heads that are used in genital wart cases. Genital warts are removed by cautery, and as they are burned up, the smoke produced by the cautery can contain viral particles that could potentially lodge in the OR staff's nose, which could conceivably cause genital warts to grow out of their noses! To combat this issue, a large self-contained respirator hood is worn during the genital wart cases.

I told the anesthesiologist that this case was not going to be like a genital wart case at all, but some small dinky-doo case where the hood would not be needed. (We don't have those hoods available in the children's day surgery anyway.) The child had about five growths on his eyelid that looked more like small skin tags, and the surgeon removed them by cutting them off with scissors and then cauterizing them. An absorbable suture was placed in the largest wound. The suture will dissolve on its own after about five days so it won't need to be removed.

Chapter
13

We had so much fun working Dr. R.'s ENT block last Wednesday! The staff, including the anesthesiologist, were all top-notch people to work with, who liked to tease each other as well, so it was a very fun morning. We were so deep in conversation with each other during a case that we were unaware that the surgeon had removed a jewelry bead that the child had put in her ear. While the surgeon looked in the other ear, I realized we had missed the event, and commented on wanting to see the bead. Dr. R. was clearly disappointed that we had not been paying attention to him when he had removed the bead. Dr. R. showed us the bead he had removed, and without missing a beat, we all oohed and aahed over what a marvelous job he had done! He turned a little red, and even looked a little embarrassed, which was very unusual for him. It was such a fun morning!

I was reminiscing with a friend on the phone the other day, and I remembered another funny story from the past. Years ago, I worked with Dr. C., a semi-crusty, no-nonsense, very competent surgeon. In elective pediatric cases, our hospital had the policy that at least one of the parents was required to be at the hospital before, and during the operation. This enabled the surgeon to be able to talk to the parent before their child had surgery, as well as a parent was present during the operation in case a problem occurred, or the surgeon needed to consult with the parents over a change needed in the surgical operation.

On this particular day, a newer nurse working on the med-surg floor had told the parents before the operation had taken place, that they had time to run home and shower, and collect some of their clothes and personal items. The parents had still not returned when it was time to take their child to surgery. Unfortunately, now their child's operation would have to be delayed, while waiting for the parents to return.

I went up to the medical-surgical floor where the child was, to confirm with the floor nurses that the parents really were not there. While I was at the nursing station along with some of the floor nurses, the phone rang. We could all guess it was Dr. C. calling, angry over the fact that his surgery was being delayed. The nurses looked at the ringing phone with dread. "Do you want me to answer the phone?" I asked. "Yes, please!" they begged. I picked up the receiver and sure enough, it was Dr. C., who was furious. The nice thing was that since I hadn't actually done anything wrong, Dr. C. couldn't really yell at me.

I commiserated with Dr. C. about the situation, and he finally hung up in frustration. A day or two later, I was working again with Dr. C., and we had the exact same situation occur! This time, the child was very ill. Because the child was so ill and needed the surgery right away, I talked to my nursing director, and found out from her that if the surgeon would declare the case as an emergent case, we could proceed with the surgery, without the parents being present. After relaying this information to Dr. C., he declared the case emergent, and we went ahead with the child's operation. The child did very well, and truly needed the operation immediately.

As luck would have it, the very next scheduled case in the block was also with Dr. C., and the parents were missing on this case as well! The nature of this case was not emergent at all. The child was very stable. Dr C. saw me in the hallway, waved his hand in the air, and declared that this elective case was also an emergency. I went and talked to my nursing director explaining the situation, and she said that if the surgeon declares the case an emergency, even if it really is not, we still proceed as if it is an emergency. We did the case, and Dr. C., with his new-found information, never had to wait again for parents to arrive to perform their child's operation!

Every year, an organization called JCAHO (Joint Commission on Accreditation of Healthcare Organizations) comes to inspect the hospital. JCAHO is strangely not a government entity, but a private one that was started years ago by the health professions. A visit from JCAHO instills fear and paranoia on everyone's part, and this year was no exception. The reason for that fear is that the organization rates your facility, and if your hospital doesn't make a certain cut, then the hospital will no longer receive reimbursement income from the government for Medicaid and Medicare patients, which makes up a large part of the hospital's patient population. I think it is strange that JCAHO always announces to the hospital the window of time that they plan to show up and survey the practices performed at that facility! Why not show up unannounced, and see how the place is run without any forewarning?

On Tuesday morning at staff meeting, it was announced that

JCAHO was on the hospital campus, and would be there for the week. The staff silently freaked out, hoping they would not be their next victim. Several people made up the JCAHO team, and they could ask you as an employee, any question they wanted to. What do you do in case of a fire? Where are your nearest fire extinguishers? How do you properly use the fire extinguisher? How would you find a certain policy of the hospital for me? Etcetera, etcetera, etcetera. Needless to say, when JCAHO was at the hospital, most of the nurses hid, but some unfortunate nurse would be followed through his or her case, where the JCAHO staff would watch the circulator bring in the patient, place monitors, prep the patient, listen to the time-out that was performed before the surgery, watch to see whether the nurse used gel every time before entering and exiting the room, whether her mask was on her face, or off her face (you couldn't let it dangle down on your neck), how the room was cleaned between cases, and so forth.

On Wednesday at morning report, it was announced that JCAHO would be in all the OR's that day for sure. All morning in day surgery, while we went through our cases, we waited for JCAHO to appear. Sure enough, in the afternoon with only one more case to go, the JCAHO entourage arrived with clipboards in their hands, and the show was about to begin!

Just then, another RN appeared, and told me that he had been sent over to send me home! When the OR gets slow, some of the staff is sent home. Staff are sent home according to a 'low census' list that is made up each day by interested staff calling in to get on the list. I couldn't believe my luck at being sent home at this very opportune time!!!!

I told the male RN, "Jay, I could kiss you, I am so happy!"

With that I grabbed his shoulders with both of my hands, and kissed the air about a foot away from his face. He asked me why I was so ecstatic. I told him that JCAHO had just arrived! His face looked incredulous! He had been across the street in the main OR while JCAHO had been over there all morning, and he had spent the entire morning hiding out from them, only to land right in their midst at the children's day surgery!

I found out a few days later, what had happened when JCAHO had come into my room after Jay had taken over. They wanted in particular to hear the 'time-out' performed. I later heard from the scrub-tech that it was the longest 'time-out' given in history! The surgeon dryly commented to me that it was like a story being read to you. Part of the 'time-out' is for everyone to introduce themselves to each other, if they don't know each other. That day, everyone introduced themselves to each other, even though they already knew each other very well!

When I went back to work the next week, it was a hundred times more relaxing knowing JCAHO was gone for another year, and we could go back to giving our usual excellent care. When you are obsessing over your performance of small individual tasks, along with being nervous, you lose sight of taking care of the actual patient. How is your patient doing while you are performing a ten-minute time-out? Does the patient benefit from being under anesthesia an extra ten minutes? Safety is great, and sometimes practices need to be improved, but I think that common sense needs to be included in all of it as well.

I remember another incident with JCAHO involving myself, that happened year ago. JCAHO was coming, as they come every year. Our nursing director had drilled into us to answer their questions, but not to volunteer any more information than was necessary. As fate would have it, that year the JCAHO group came into my room where a dental procedure was taking place. We were all terrified until I looked at them, and thought, "Hey, they are just people." One JCAHO member geared up, and asked me what my role with the patient had been prior to surgery. There, against the back OR wall, were both my nursing manager, and my nursing director, who always tour around with JCAHO when they visit the hospital. Both my manager and director's eyes were filled with terror!

After having had cancer, along with its subsequent multiple years of treatment, I had noticed that at times it was as if I had become two separate entities......one was the controlled person that usually governed myself, and the other side of me was the wild person who did crazy things I would not usually have done. I could feel the crazy person taking over, and the controlled part of me thought "Oh, no ....what will my manager and director think?"

In high school I had taken oral showmanship, and had lost big-time once, before going on to win a year later. I found out from that experience, that the difference in winning in showmanship is to share with the judges all of the knowledge you possess. I also had learned that the person doing the talking has control of the floor.

I started by telling my JCAHO interviewer all about my interview with the parents before surgery. I explained that I tried to bond with the parents by introducing myself and shaking their hand. I also explained how I asked the parents all of the pertinent questions; such as their child's npo status, allergies, and as a safeguard, what operation was being performed on their child that day. I continued telling the JCAHO interviewer that the child's identity bracelet was checked and matched with the child's name and birth date; as well as having the parents confirm the birth date. Then, I went on to explain how I told the parents where they would wait during the operation, how the surgeon would be out to talk to them afterwards, and how their child would go to recovery after the operation was complete. I further explained how the parents would meet back up with their child when the child was brought out from recovery, and that the parents and their child would then return to the same room that they had been admitted to initially. There, the child would finish their recovery before being discharged home.

I just kept going on and on with how I positioned the child, placed monitors, started the IV, helped with intubation and did the time-out. All the while, my manager and director had sheer terror written on their faces with the knowledge that I had gone completely renegade to their previous directions. When I ran out of things to say about myself, I started to explain the procedure the dentist was performing, and how he accomplished it. Finally, I was done. The JCAHO interviewer seemed very pleased, and the whole entourage left. A few seconds after leaving, my director scrambled back into the room and said, "That was amazing!" The dentist said innocently, "I couldn't have explained the procedure I am doing any better myself!"

The only person in the room who was onto me was the anesthesiologist. He looked at me and said dryly, "That was good." He knew exactly what I had done. I heard later from my manager that the JCAHO interviewer had been very impressed with how friendly and professional I had been! 😊

I was working with an ENT surgeon who did about eight hundred cases a year, and who I worked with on a weekly basis in the pediatric day surgery area. Across from our room was the second operating room in the day surgery area. A dentist was performing dental work there, and all went smoothly in that dental case, until the case was over. At the conclusion of the dental case, the circulator Lisa, noticed that the eight-year-old boy was missing one of his front teeth, and the area where the tooth had been, was bleeding a little. Before the case had started neither the parents, nor the boy had mentioned that one of his front teeth was loose. Now the search began in earnest to find the missing tooth. The hope was that the tooth had fallen in amongst the bedding somewhere, but it could not be found.

This meant that the tooth had either gone down the child's airway, or into the esophagus and stomach. If the tooth ended up in the stomach the child would be fine, but if the tooth had inadvertently gone down into the airway it could cause a great deal of trouble, including a possible abscess in the lungs! X-ray was called, and a portable X-ray was taken while the boy remained asleep. The tooth was spotted lying in the upper airway just above the epiglottis, and the anesthesiologist removed the tooth by grasping it with a pair of long Magill forceps. Happy Day! What a great job Lisa had done by noticing the missing tooth, and by going the extra mile to ensure that the tooth was not in the airway, which it had been!

Confidentiality is a big deal at the hospital. No other employee is allowed to view anyone's record unless you are working with them as a patient. In the past, employees have looked up another employee's records sometimes purely out of concern for the person, when they heard that they had been admitted to the hospital for some reason. This is not tolerated at all anymore, and an employee will lose their job for accessing any record that is not directly related to a legitimate reason, such as having that person as your patient. This even includes looking up your own personal information, which I have always thought was a bit ridiculous.

If one of your patients happens to be an employee and you are legitimately accessing their information, a special window will come up on the computer screen warning you that you had better have a legitimate reason to view that record. If you proceed and confirm to the computer that you want to view that employee's record, it is called 'breaking the glass.' In the OR you will hear the anesthesiologist talk about how they had to 'break the glass' to view a patient's record. Since the company we work for owns multiple hospitals and clinics, the patient may not even work at the same facility we are at, so it would be very unusual for us to even know the other employee.

Chapter

14

The OR has its own scheduling department. The people there schedule the various cases that are to take place in the OR. Since each room in the OR may have multiple surgeons throughout the day, each case is assigned a time to begin and to end. This time is based on how long the surgeon usually takes to finish a similar case. If the same surgeon has multiple cases and is following himself, if one of his cases runs overtime, it is no problem. A problem arises, when another surgeon is supposed to start his or her case, and the anesthesiologist, circulating RN, and the scrub person, are all still working on the previous case that has gone overtime.

If other staff can be found, then another team will at least start the case for the surgeon. If no other staff is available, then that operation will have to be delayed, and usually the surgeon is given a heads-up about the delay before they show up at the hospital.

Today, I was working in my usual ENT block and we were running a little late, but our last patient was in the OR, when the anesthesiologist got a text on his phone that said his other patient was waiting for him across the street in the main OR! He had been assigned another case across the street in the main OR at noon, but at noon he was still working with us on our last patient in the day surgery area.

The nurse who had brought the adult patient into the OR without checking on the availability of the anesthesiologist had recently graduated from the last OR nurse residency. The anesthesiologist directed her to take the patient back to the med-surg floor, to await him finishing his cases with us. This was a big mistake that she will probably not make again! I hope that she is rugged enough not to begin to hate her new job and quit!

Dr. H. was so good at being an anesthesiologist, that it almost seemed like he wasn't even doing anything while he was in the OR with you! His patients went right to sleep, they woke up effortlessly after the surgery was done, and he was always involved in any fun conversation that took place during the procedure. He was masterfully skilled. One time, he had injured one of his legs somehow, and one of my favorite memories of him was he took a hospital stool on wheels that a surgeon might use to sit on during surgery, and used it to hold up his injured leg on by propping his knee on the stool. Then with crutches, he would quickly wheel and hop his way down the surgery hallways!

He never gave it a thought of how he looked when he entered the patient's pre-op room to talk to the parents regarding their child's surgery that morning. The parent's disconcerted faces showed their concern over getting a one-legged anesthesiologist, but he was so skilled that I would have been glad to have had him as my anesthesiologist even with one leg!

One morning, I had been asked to help start an IV on an adult. Since I was quite proficient at starting IV's on babies and children, I figured their request would be a very easy one to accomplish on an adult. Multiple people surrounded the thirty-something-year-old male, all trying to find an IV site. I was surprised to find that the patient was conscious and talking, which I found out later, was at his request. To put it mildly, he was not happy with our services, and was giving us a lot of negative feedback. Looking at his hands and arms, I was amazed that no veins were visible, and that he had small round scars up and down his arms from using drugs. Tiring of listening to his verbal sauce, the anesthesiologist gassed the patient via his mask, so that we didn't have to listen to his diatribe any longer. I was never able to get an IV started on him!

The next time I was summoned into a room with multiple people trying to start an IV, I knew it would be a difficult process to start an IV. An anesthesiologist was at the head of the patient managing the anesthetized patient's airway, but several other anesthesiologists were there as well, trying to start the patient's IV.

Dr. H., who was one of my favorite anesthesiologists, was positioned at the patient's left foot. Used IV catheters hung limply in different spots all over the patient's body, witnesses of futile attempts to gain IV access. Jokingly, I quietly told Dr. H., "I am filled with trepidation just seeing all of you!" Dr. H. quipped back that I should be, and assigned me to the area of the patient's right foot. Looking at the foot, I could see there were no possibilities for starting an IV, but looking up--there on the patient's leg were two beautiful veins--side by side. I asked Dr, H., "You don't care where I put the IV?" "No," he answered emphatically. They had been desperately trying to start an IV for over thirty minutes, and were thinking about canceling the case. Quickly, I put an IV successfully in one of the leg veins, and to everyone's amazement, especially the surgeon's, I announced my success. "Do you have time to tape the IV down so I can get back to my room?" I asked. "Sure," Dr. H. said, smiling broadly.

It is unusual for one of the staff members in the OR to be tossed out of the room by the surgeon, but it does happen occasionally. One day, a dentist was working and Lisa was giving a lunch break to Laura, the circulator. During that time, Lisa had somehow made the dentist mad, but he obviously wasn't paying that much attention, because as Laura came wandering back from lunch and reentered her OR room, the dentist told Laura, not Lisa, that she was banned from the room! I came upon Laura dazedly wandering in the hall outside her OR room. As Laura told me about her predicament, I found it especially funny, as she was not even the person who had made the dentist mad!

Another time, a crabby old ENT surgeon told the scrub-tech who was working with him that morning to leave the room. Later, the same surgeon feeling badly, cut a rose from the rose garden on campus, and offered it to the scrub-tech as a peace offering! The surgeon was apparently unaware that cutting a rose which was the property of the hospital, was considered by the hospital to be an act of theft!

I never was tossed out by a surgeon, but there were a few times I would have welcomed it--look at the bright side--you have gotten out of working in a difficult room!

She was five years old, and still had the remnants of pink nail polish on her toes. One week ago, she had been playing at home, and doing all the things a little girl would do. Now, she had severe brain damage caused by cerebral edema. She also had renal failure, and her legs were black, leathery, and mummified. She was here in the OR to have both of her legs amputated. She had suffered from DKA: Diabetic ketoacidosis. Her DKA had been caused by her undiagnosed type-one diabetes. The symptoms children typically present when they develop type-one diabetes are an excessive thirst, and frequent urination. Weight loss is also another symptom. Left untreated, nausea and vomiting begin. Her family had all been ill with a virus and had nausea and vomiting, so when their daughter began to vomit, drink lots of fluid, and urinate massive amounts, no one in her family had brought her into the hospital. Only when she became lethargic and unresponsive, was she brought in, and by then the damage was severe. This child was in the worst-case scenario.... alive, and yet unable to ever recover to normal levels of brain function; yet still with enough primitive brain function to breathe on her own. It was a pure tragedy in every sense of the word. Fortunately, we did not see this type of scenario in the OR very often.

My thirty-five-year old son called saying he thought he had appendicitis. After denying that we needed to come pick him up, I told my son to drive to the hospital that I worked for, and that we would meet him there. By the time my husband and I arrived at the hospital, my son was already there, with a nurse taking some blood samples from him. Feelings of overwhelming vulnerability came rushing back to me, as we sat helplessly in the emergency room. After a cat scan confirmed the diagnosis of appendicitis, my son was scheduled for emergency surgery.

After personally having had two bouts with cancer and undergoing chemotherapy for years, I was all too aware of how helpless you feel when you are the patient. Will the staff that you happen to get be good? Is this really the best course of treatment that you should be taking? I was comforted with the fact that the OR staff was well known to me, and that they were for the most part, all excellent. My son was moved from the emergency room to a hospital room to await his surgery.

The surgeon arrived, and after going over my son's condition, the pros and cons of having surgery, the surgeon then filled out the consent form. I recognized the surgeon from the OR as one that worked with adult patients. Looking out into the hallway, the surgeon muttered that you could never find a nurse when you needed one! He needed a nurse to sign the consent as a witness. I piped up that I was a nurse, and that I would sign. (I realize that it is not proper for the mother to sign the consent, but I wanted my son to have his operation quickly) While I signed the consent, Dr. W. asked me, "where do you work?" I told him that I worked there in the OR, and that I had actually scrubbed previously on two of his cases with him, but that usually I only worked with children. Now true disbelief filled his face. "Why would they have you scrub for me if you worked in pediatrics?" he asked. "They were desperate," I replied. Dr. W. left to prepare for the surgery. Nurses that I knew from the OR showed up to transport my son, and we all headed for the OR doors. There we were met by an anesthesiologist, that of course, I knew. My son did very well in surgery, and I felt that the care he received was very good.

The next morning, I saw one of the nurses who had been with my son during his operation, and she told me how Dr. W. had asked everyone in the OR if they knew me. Even after they had all confirmed that they knew me, he would ask any other person coming into the OR room, including another anesthesiologist who replaced the original one, if she knew who I was! He still couldn't believe that he had ever worked with me. This was amusing to me, as every day during surgery, different staff come in and relieve other staff members for lunches, breaks, etcetera. We all wear so much garb including masks, hair covering, and protective eye wear that it is common to see people from the OR later dressed in street clothes, and not be able to recognize them!

All of the nurses I told the story of Dr W. not recognizing me, got a big kick out of it. It is always funny when someone doesn't believe what you are telling them. As I told the other nurses, if I was making up a fantasy life it wouldn't be as a scrub nurse in the OR! The next day, I noticed that Dr. W. was operating in the OR; however, I was in a surgery with a pediatric case. As a joke, another nurse wandered down the hall and poked her head in my room wondering if I was going to go down the hall and say "Hi!" to Dr. W.! For the next several days, that same nurse would say, "Hey stranger!" to me every time she saw me!

The case was about to start, and I had just plugged in the cautery cord which had been handed off to me by the scrub-tech. Without realizing it, my right foot had become tangled in the other sturdy cord which went from the grounding pad I had applied to the patient into the cautery machine. As I stepped back, the cord pulled at my right foot and I was caught off-balance. After trying to regain my balance, and seeing it was futile, I tried to fall as gracefully as possible.... if that is possible! Everyone in the room was horrified as I hit the ground, and my glasses flew off my head, and skidded across the floor. When you are sixty-years old and hit the deck, everyone is mortified! To help me, the surgeon offered to stop operating, and wondered if I shouldn't go to the ER to be checked out. I assured everyone that I was fine, but they continued to ask me throughout the completion of the case if I was really fine.

The last time I had fallen in the OR, I was much younger, and the reaction in the room had been the complete opposite. Back then, after realizing I had survived the fall, my friend who was scrubbing the case and the anesthesiologist both started cracking up! The neurologist who was operating at the time, merely looked over his glasses at me sprawled on the floor, assured himself that I wasn't a head injury he would have to get involved with, and kept on operating!

Once in a while I do a case involving an adult, instead of a child. My patient was ninety-two years old, and she had previously had a cancerous lesion in the middle of her forehead removed, and then treated with radiation. Unfortunately, she now had a hole in her skin on her forehead that was about two-and-one-half inches in diameter, with her skull bone showing beneath it. She was here today to have the skin pulled over the skull. To my distress, she still had a metal ring on her finger which seemed fairly loose, but because of her arthritic knuckle, I couldn't get the ring to slide off of her finger. As I have mentioned previously, you don't want any metal on your body before surgery because of the electrical cautery used during surgery. A few years back, I had watched another nurse remove a ring from a patient's finger with some string and lubricant. I had also recently gotten my father's ring off of his swollen finger using the same trick, so I will describe it here. Obtain a piece of dental floss or another piece of very strong, thin string about eighteen inches in length. Slip the floss under the ring and then fold it in half so both ends of the floss meet together. Knot the ends of the floss together well, as there will be a lot of pressure on the knot. Put soap, lotion or any other lubricant on the finger with the ring on it. Pull down gently on the knotted floss in a continuous circular motion around the entire finger so that the floss moves around the ring as you pull. Make sure you ask the person to tell you if at any time this process is hurting them, so that you can stop if you need to. This method will not work in every case, but it is very successful at removing rings most of the time!

A nurse called for me to come help her in her room. Entering the room, you could feel some tension. Her patient was having a mastectomy and then reconstruction. Upon completing the mastectomy, a count was performed, and one of the raytec sponges was missing. In an operation, there are two types of cloth sponges that surgeons use to wipe away blood. One is a large sponge called a 'lap,' and a smaller sponge is called a 'raytec.' Both have radiofrequency tags embedded in each one, so that a large circular wand can be passed over the surgical site at the end of the operation to ensure that neither type of sponge is left in the patient after surgery. This radiofrequency wand is meant only as a backup to the count that is performed after each surgery, meaning that the count should be correct, and then you use the wand to confirm that there is nothing left behind. The problem is that if the count is incorrect; meaning something is missing, then an X-ray has to be performed on the patient before they leave the OR, to ensure that nothing has been left inside the patient during surgery. This is traumatic to everyone except the patient, who is still asleep on the operating table. If an X-ray has to be done, the surgeon is unhappy, and extra paperwork must be done by the circulator, because of this potentially serious problem. Plus it really bothers the staff to know that the raytec is missing somewhere....but where?

In this case, which had used a lot of 'laps' and 'rays,' the nurse and scrub technician were recounting the sponges to try and find the missing sponge, and avoid the hassle of having to call for an X-ray. I helped look through the forty or so raytec sponges, which had been placed in long clear plastic bags which hung from a tall pole mounted on wheels. Each clear bag had ten envelopes which each held one used sponge, so the entire bag held a total of ten sponges, for easy counting. We searched each individual envelope to determine that only one raytec had been placed there. Next, I searched the bucket where all the bloody 'laps' had been placed to determine that the missing raytec had not accidentally been placed with them. After that, I started to look at any small piles of trash that had been left when someone had scrubbed into the case, and left behind glove wrappers, etc. No raytec could be discovered!

Having had some experience at having missing raytec sponges in the past, I next started going through the large trash container. I placed a used paper surgical gown from the trash on the floor next to the trash, and started putting the contents of the trash on top of it. About halfway through the trash there it was--one wet, folded-over raytec! The relief in the room was palpable as I produced the prize. Whether the raytec had stuck to the surgeon's gown when he took the gown off and threw it away, or whether he had it in his hand and without thinking threw it in the trash will never be known. In the past, I have even seen a raytec sponge folded inside a pair of surgeon's gloves as he removed them inside-out, and placed them in the trash! Those are even harder to detect in the trash as they are inside the glove, and not visible.

Days later, another nurse who was more brilliant than I, suggested that the wand could have been passed over the trash, which would have set off the alarm, confirming to you that the missing raytec is in the trash, before you even began to look in the trash for the raytec. What a great idea!

Chapter

15

Fire is a really big deal in the OR; bigger than I ever imagined, until I had one in the room that I was in one day! I was learning how to scrub eye cases that day. Two circulators were working in the room that day--an experienced nurse on the computer, and a relatively new nurse doing patient care. In some eye cases a battery-powered hand-held cautery is used. We have two types of battery-powered hand-held cautery; a low-heat, and a high-heat cautery. In this particular quick case, the surgeon required a high-heat cautery stick. After using the cautery, he placed it on the mayo stand which is an elevated metal tray which holds the surgical instruments. Unfortunately, he placed the now very hot tip of the cautery device onto a cotton raytec sponge. Immediately a small yellow flame erupted on the raytec sponge. I'm sure both the scrub-tech and my eyes were wide with surprise at seeing a tiny fire on the mayo stand, but the scrub-tech quickly grabbed the burning raytec, and put it in our basin of water sitting nearby on our back table.

With the fire completely doused, we didn't think a lot more about it until the room was cleaned, and the trash was removed, and thrown in a large bin containing all the other morning's trash. As the day continued, I mentioned to the other nurses that we probably should fill out an incident report. Knowing our manager would be concerned about the potential for a fire to start in the trash, and being certain that there was no possibility of that, we put the report in her folder in her office which she wouldn't see until the next day. By then the trash would have been removed, the building would still be standing, and all would be well. WRONG!

What I didn't know, was that the State had to be notified when any fire occurred, and lots of paperwork filled out! Who knew? We had never been given a class on fire aftermath-- only on how to save the patient in the event a fire occurred. Our patient was never even in any danger! No one in management ever raked me over the coals over the incident but the new, less-experienced nurse took a lot of heat over it. She quit working in the OR shortly thereafter, which was a shame.

One morning, we had performed a bowel surgery on a young infant which weighed only eight pounds. As we started to 'close' or finish the case, I began to count instruments since the very tiny body cavity of the abdomen had been open. After counting instruments, we started to count the 'softs,' which included the raytec and lap sponges. We were missing one raytec sponge. I scoured the room, and we repeated the count several times with the same result--one raytec sponge was missing. Meanwhile the surgeon was busy closing up the infant's abdomen. None of us in the room could quite believe a raytec could have been left in such a tiny body cavity. The anesthesiologist had the brilliant idea of getting a sterile cover for the wand device which could detect raytec and lap sponges, and so we the passed the wand device over the baby's abdomen. Sure enough, the wand alarmed as it was held over the baby's abdomen!

The surgeon reopened and went into the baby's abdominal

cavity, fished around for a few minutes, and then pulled out the missing raytec sponge! Ever since that case, I have had a healthy respect for even very tiny places on the body having the ability to retain an instrument or sponge!

Sometimes our pranks in the OR can go a little too far--one in particular comes to mind. I was working with Dr. D., an anesthesiologist who loves to tease me every chance he gets. We were just starting a case. Dr. D. had administered the inhalant agent sevoflurane via a mask to get our patient sedated, and I had just finished putting in an IV. Next, propofol, an IV sedation drug, was going to be administered. He handed me the filled syringe, and I pushed the propofol through my newly started IV. Dr. D. looked at me in alarm and stated, "You didn't just give all of that propofol, did you?"

Images of the patient with no respirations, and a possible full code raced through my mind. I was determined to keep the patient alive at all costs. I could envision getting the crash cart, calling a code, and bagging the patient to keep his respirations going for as long as it took. Fortunately, propofol has a short half-life. All of these thoughts flashed through my mind in only a second or two. Then I heard Dr. D. laugh, and I realized thankfully that I had been 'had.' The surgeon commented dryly that I had turned as 'white as a ghost.' I have never pushed propofol since, without confirming first, that the anesthesiologist wants me to give the entire amount!

Kate, the scrub-tech, got Dr. D. back for me within a few weeks. She was in a case with Dr. D., and she had a sterile single basin that rested in a stand on wheels. She didn't need the basin for the case, and when Dr. D. got close, she inconspicuously pushed the basin into him. He was horrified that he had contaminated the sterile field. Kate said, "That one was for Sheila!" Payback completed!

I went to pick up an adult patient for surgery in the afternoon. The gentleman sat in his hospital bed with something playing on his smart phone, and his female companion sat next to him. His surgery had been scheduled for one in the afternoon, and now it was a little after two in the afternoon. As I began to talk to him, he ignored me, and continued to look at his phone for a while, and then grudgingly turned it off. The woman mumbled that we were a whole hour late, and it was clear that they were both upset by the fact that he was not having his surgery exactly on time. I apologized that we were late, and that I appreciated their patience. Finally, the man answered some of the questions I had regarding his health, and I took him to surgery. Most people have this same attitude regarding their scheduled operations. If they are not taken to surgery exactly when they are scheduled, they get upset. What people need to know is that if you are scheduled for a surgery, especially in the afternoon, it is possible and even probable, that your surgery could be delayed.

Earlier that morning, I had worked helping four different patients with their surgeries. Although the surgery times for starting and ending are scheduled, we don't just stop working on a patient when their scheduled time is up! We continue to work with them until their surgery is truly finished. Can you imagine stopping work on a patient when his scheduled time is up, even if his abdomen is still open? This may delay the next case, and so on. I have also seen where we are ready early to take a patient back to surgery. This can happen because the previous surgeries took less time than scheduled, or because one of the surgeries cancelled, because of a patient unexpectedly becoming ill the morning of their surgery. Occasionally, patients don't show up for their scheduled surgeries. If you are going to have a surgery, go with the mindset that your surgery might take place early, but more likely, that your surgery may be delayed; especially if your surgery is scheduled to begin in the afternoon. If your surgery is delayed, and you are not picked up for surgery right on time, it is not a personal affront to you! I can assure you that the OR crew is hard at work, and not just in a back room somewhere having drinks and laughs while you wait!

Daniel was a four-year-old redhead, who had come in to have his tonsils and adenoids removed. Before I saw him, there had been some discussion between the anesthesiologist and the surgeon over some bruising the parents had noticed lately. The surgeon dismissed it as irrelevant. When I saw the child, his bruising pattern on the front of his legs seemed within normal limits for a child of that age. The thing that concerned me was his breathing. He was asleep on the stretcher, but his breathing was more rapid than it should have been in my opinion. I asked the parents about his breathing, and they stated that this was normal for him. Very enlarged tonsils and adenoids can obstruct your airway, which would tend to increase your effort in breathing, so my gut told me that we were probably going to have difficulties with this patient, but that he very much needed the surgery in an effort to ease his breathing. When I brought Daniel back into the OR he was in a deep sleep, and didn't awaken when he was moved from the stretcher to the OR bed. His lethargy concerned me, and I asked the RN who had brought Daniel from pre-surgery to us, if he had been awake at all. She assured me that he had been awake and appropriate, when she had brought him back. The surgery proceeded along without incident, and Daniel did indeed have huge tonsils and adenoids that needed to be removed. The surgeon did notice that Daniel had more bleeding than normal; however, it really is true that redheads tend to bleed more than other people, so that did not seem unusual at the time either.

After the surgery, Daniel was taken to recovery where he proceeded to bleed unusually, concerning the recovery nurses. The anesthesiologist as well as the surgeon were called back to the recovery room to see this patient. We, as the OR staff, were preparing for another surgeon's case, but held off opening the room for the other surgeon for a while, just in case Daniel needed to come back to the OR to treat a post-operative bleed, which we sometimes infrequently needed to do. The surgeon declined the need to bring Daniel back to surgery, and so we proceeded on with our day.

We later found out that Daniel continued to have problems with bleeding, so he was admitted to the hospital for observation overnight. During the night he had a seizure, and was moved to the Pediatric Intensive Care Unit. After many tests were performed, it turned out that Daniel had undiagnosed leukemia! What devastating news for the parents! First, they have all these problems after surgery, and then to find out that the problem is even worse than they imagined; when their child is diagnosed with leukemia! Daniel's leukemia was so severe that chemotherapy was started immediately. Normally, chemotherapy is not given to a patient who has had surgery for at least two to three weeks. This is because chemotherapy disrupts cell division, and for healing to take place you need cell division to occur.

In hindsight, it would have been better if Benjamin's

leukemia had been diagnosed first before ever having surgery, and yet would he have been diagnosed if he hadn't had the surgery, and gotten into difficulty? These are some of the difficult questions and circumstances that exist in medicine.

Today at work one of the nurses, TJ, who is a real character, decided to wear a man's hospital hat backwards, so it tied at the top of his head, making him look ridiculous! In the operating room our heads need to be covered completely, and after the state came through last year, the OR got dinged in the state's report because some of the staff's hair was showing.

To comply, one male staff member went so far as to shave his hairy chest! Now that is dedication! Management told us that we needed to wear several hats, if that is what it took to cover all of our hair. Now, staff members are getting creative in a passive aggressive way with their hat attire, just like TJ. TJ's scrub person told him that she wasn't working with him if he didn't change his hat, because he looked so ridiculous. He changed it.

Another nurse was told by managers that his hair was showing, so he took one hat to cover his head, and placed another hat on top of that one which covered even the hair of his eyebrows! With his mask over his face, and eyewear on to protect his eyes, he looked quite the sight! Many of the staff are quite the characters, which makes the job even more fun!

I was circulating in a block with a petite female dentist, Dr. B., who had immigrated many years ago from India. The atmosphere in the OR room was relaxed and pleasant as Dr. B. proceeded to repair the child's teeth. Into the room came the RN TJ, who was in between cases. He was looking for someone to visit with, and he and the male anesthesiologist soon bonded over discussing some of their hunting experiences from the past. TJ talked about his experiences hunting deer, as well as different types of wild birds, including pheasants. At times, the conversation between TJ and the anesthesiologist became a little gruesome for Dr. B. and I, as we were both definitely not the hunting type. TJ enjoyed hearing my occasional verbal groans as he regaled us with his varying hunting experiences. TJ went on to talk about how one time, he had happened to come upon a large tree that had blown down in a storm, which had contained an eagle's nest. Inside of the eagle's nest, several small dog collars were discovered. I let out another groan as I realized the eagle had devoured someone's precious little dogs! TJ was really enjoying having fun with us.

After listening to all of this, the usually quiet Dr. B. spoke up and said to TJ with her lilting Indian accent, "Thank-you for your visit." In other words, get lost! It only took a fraction of a second for TJ to realize that he was being booted from the room. TJ grinned, and left. TJ later went on to become Dr. B,'s favorite circulator — go figure!

Today was a really bad day. It ended with the surgeon being furious with me! We had been doing a laparoscopic appendectomy. In a laparoscopic case, an incision is made in the belly button, (umbilicus) and a long needle is inserted. This needle is hooked up to tubing which goes off the field to a machine that can pump carbon dioxide through the tubing into the patient's abdomen. After the abdomen is filled with gas (which lessens the likelihood that the surgeon could accidentally stab and injure another structure inside the abdomen), the surgeon then removes the needle, and places a trocar in the same hole made in the umbilicus.

The trocar is a plastic tube with a pointed end which goes into the patient. The other end has an attachment to hook up the carbon dioxide gas to it. Two other incisions are made-- one on the left side of the patient, and another on the lower left side. Trocars are placed in each of those two incisions so that other laparoscopic instruments can be used. Even though your appendix is usually located on the right side of your body, by working on the left side, the surgeon can point the instruments toward the right side where the appendix is located. A long scope is placed through the hole inside the trocar on the left side, and a camera is attached to the scope so that the surgeon can visualize what is inside the abdomen by looking up at the viewing monitors hanging from the ceiling. A very bright light box supplies light through a cable to the scope, which lights up the inside of the abdomen so the surgeon can see. The surgeon uses a long staple gun through a trocar to detach the appendix from the intestines. The staples will stay in the patient for the rest of their life.

A long instrument with a deflated plastic bag is put down inside a trocar, and the bag is opened. The appendix is placed inside the bag, the bag is closed, and then pulled up through the incision in the abdomen. With the appendix out, the light box and carbon dioxide gas need to be turned off, since they are no longer needed. The light is very powerful, and can become very hot. After the appendix came out, I definitely remember turning off the gas, and I thought I had turned off the light; but at the end of the surgery, the surgeon cussed, and was furious, because the light had inadvertently stayed on; the lighted cord had been placed on top of the draped patient, and had burned a hole through the sterile drape! We were so lucky that the patient did not get burned or have a fire start! I, of course, felt HORRIBLE! The next time I do a laparoscopic case, I will pull the cable end out of the light box for double insurance that the light is off, and cannot burn through the drapes. It is at times like this that I seriously think about getting another job!

Chapter
16

One of my favorite surgeons, Dr. G., had a long 'block' or group of surgeries, and I was very happy to have been assigned to be the circulator for that room. The surgical-tech for that room was E., who was not one of my most favorite people to work with, but I was still excited to be in that block.

The morning started with an emergent case--a testicular torsion. A genetic defect had allowed for this boy's spermatic cord to twist, which then cut off the blood supply to his testicle. It is an emergent case, because if the blood flow is not restored quickly to the testicle, the testicle will die and have to be removed.

Fortunately for this young man, the color of his testicle went from a blackish color to a nice pink color once the spermatic cord was untwisted, and the surgeon tacked the testicle down, so that this could never happen again. He also explored the other testicle, as there is a thirty-percent chance that it also has the same defect, and needs to be tacked down as well.

As the morning progressed, E., who was a scrub-tech with many years of experience, kept asking me what instruments the surgeon needed to do the next case with, because I frequently scrubbed with this surgeon as well. I didn't mind helping E. by telling her what instruments she needed, but I had a lot on my mind performing the circulator's role, and I found it slightly annoying to have to do my job, as well as help with someone else's, especially an experienced scrub tech. Our second case involved a tiny baby, and I felt that I had been very fortunate to have started his IV with one try. After the case was finished, the anesthesiologist showed me where blood was backing up into the IV tubing. She felt that somehow, I had put the IV catheter into an artery, instead of a vein, and insisted that I start another IV. We discontinued the first IV, and the sleeping baby had to be poked multiple times before I could finally get another IV catheter in successfully. Finding another IV site took quite a few minutes. Then I discovered, that there was actually nothing wrong with the original IV, but that the IV volutrol had not been vented properly by the nurse who had set it up while I was at break!

The improper venting was what had caused blood to back up into the IV tubing. The fact that this poor baby now had multiple pokes, which ended up being unnecessary, upset me. The anesthesiologist also felt bad about it, and foolish that she had not figured out what was really happening. We took the baby to recovery together, and I returned to the room to finish my charting, and set up the room for the next patient. E. spoke up, and said that I could go get my next patient. As I didn't have anything set up for my next patient, I thought her comment was a little crazy, but I let it pass.

E. appears outwardly to be very sweet and polite, but I have always wondered if there was a falseness to her sweetness, which proved to be correct a short while later. We did the next case, and after I returned to the room E. asked what she could do to make the turnovers go better.... insinuating that I was the drag on the turnover time. Well, I would have to agree that I was holding the cases up, but I felt that it was because I had people 'helping' me that didn't know what they were doing, and I had just spent an extra fifteen-minutes trying to start an IV, when the first one had turned out to have been perfectly good! E. stated proudly that she was helping our turnover time by cleaning the room with the housekeepers. She asked me if the instruments for our third case would be exactly the same as they had been for our first case. I told her no, it needed to be set up differently because there would be a second incision in the abdomen. I also told her that if she really wanted to help me speed up, she could quit asking me about how all of the instruments should be set up, as I already had a lot on my mind. Boy, did that set her off! She started banging things around, and finally got someone else to come into the room to finish her instrument set-up! For the rest of the afternoon, she wouldn't give me the time of day.

The really interesting thing to me, was that after she returned to the room, she became extra super sweet to Dr. G. One of E.'s favorite sayings that she commonly used was "that is so awesome." She said it this day as well, and would say it over and over to Dr. G., in a slow, breathy Jackie Kennedy sort of way; and he was eating it up with a spoon! Fascinating how simple most men are! Dr. G. told her how he was on the varsity tennis team when he was a freshman or sophomore in high school. She oohed and aahed over that. I never could bring myself to do all that false admiration stuff with men, but they sure seem to love it at any age. It seems that very few men can see through that. The rest of our block went the same way.... with E. giving me the cold shoulder, and with her hanging on every word that Dr. G. said, and repeatedly telling him, "that is soooo awesome!"

Management has decided that in order to try to increase the amount of our cases that start on time at eight a.m., that the patients need to be brought to the room by seven-thirty. They want our turn-over times, which is the time between when one case ends and the next case begins, to be less than twenty minutes. I think one of the major problems which increases our turn-over time here, is that they do not use people efficiently. For instance, on a daily basis, I perform lots of tasks that do not require a registered nurse to do. Putting monitors on the bed, taking time to find a pillow to put on the bed, finding a hover-mat, which is an inflatable long pillow that is used under heavy patients so that they can be moved easily after surgery, are just a few of the things I frequently find myself doing before the next case can start.

There should be other people doing those tasks, so that the nurse can perform the tasks that only she is qualified to do, such as setting up the IV fluids, getting any medications needed for the surgery, interviewing the patient, and making sure that there is a current H&P, as well as a consent that is filled out correctly for the upcoming surgery.

Today, I was helping to clean the OR room between cases, and the scrub technician berated me for cleaning, saying that I would make more housekeepers lose their job. The housekeeper overhearing the conversation, told me later how much she appreciated my help.

This same scrub-tech didn't want to open and set up the instruments for surgery too early this morning on our first case, so I told her that if the patient was ready, I was going to bring the patient back, whether she was ready or not. If she wants to horse around and eat her breakfast of oatmeal, that is her decision. The reason she doesn't want to open too early is that once the instruments are open, she has to stay in the room and guard the room, ensuring that the instrument field remains sterile. The anesthesiologist was confused as to what was going on, since the instruments weren't ready for surgery, like he expected them to be. The whole thing just leaves you with a bad feeling. The scrub-tech found someone to help her open the sterile drapes and instruments at the last minute, just before I brought the patient back to the OR.

Last week I was doing a long list of ENT cases in the children's day surgery unit where I most commonly worked. Afterwards, the surgeon was scheduled to do two cases in the main OR across the street; one was because the pediatric patient was too heavy to qualify for the day surgery area, and the other was because the patient was an adult. This surgeon has clinic hours every afternoon starting at one o'clock. On this particular day he had booked surgeries that were supposed to last to almost two o'clock! Also, if we have to move from the day surgery area to the main OR across the street, that always slows us down considerably.

After finishing the morning cases, we rushed over to do the first case across the street in the main adult OR, and I omitted writing the cases up on the white board like we do across the street in the day surgery area. The white dry erase board keeps everyone apprised of the various surgeries we are performing. This surgeon usually does about eight to ten cases in four hours, so it would be easier to make a mistake and do the wrong procedure, if we did not have each case written up on the back wall of the OR room, where everyone can easily read it.

At the beginning of the case I said the 'time-out' as usual, and announced that we were doing a tonsillectomy and adenoidectomy. Everyone agreed. The scrub-tech was behind on opening up the instruments, and had a student with her as well; so, she apparently wasn't as alert during the 'time-out' as she usually would have been. After the surgery was completed, the surgeon pronounced that he was done, and I thought that the procedure had gone too quickly, so I questioned whether he had done both the tonsillectomy and adenoidectomy. He said, "no, it was tonsils only." Our last patient across the street had been tonsils only, and I think that he was still thinking of her name and procedure, that had been written up on the white board. I told him this patient was also to have her adenoids removed as well. He didn't believe me, so I showed him the consent, and he proceeded to take out the adenoids as well.

This is a common problem in the OR; rush, rush, rush. Part of it was my fault for not writing his cases up on the board, even though it only involved two cases. Part of it was the surgeon's fault for overbooking himself when he knew he had to be at his clinic by one in the afternoon. Part of the fault belonged to the scrub-tech, who had taken more than her half-hour for lunch, and wasn't as ready as she usually was. Fortunately, the mistake was caught, and the patient had the correct, complete procedure done.

This morning, we were sitting in our lounge before work began. The OR staff has a very nice lounge, and the physicians have their own lounge. In our lounge there is a giant-sized television mounted on one wall. A large bank of windows runs alongside another wall which faces east, and has a gorgeous view. Two refrigerators and a sink line the opposite wall. Tables with chairs are on one-half of the long narrow room and on the other side are couches and chairs where the television is. Two computers are available on each end of the room, and at the far end of the room are mail cubbies for each employee. Staff congregate there in the morning, and all throughout the day to eat meals, and take their breaks and chat. Now with cell phones, a room can be filled with people all looking at their phones, and not communicating with anyone present, which is interesting!

This morning, as we hung around before the work day began at seven a.m., the fire alarms went off, and the overhead page said there was a fire outside OR room number ten! We all raced towards where the fire was supposed to be, only to find nothing there. Our director was there giving directions as she knew the hospital security staff would soon be there, and would need to put on cover overalls, as no one is usually allowed in the OR area in street clothes. A few minutes later as we had gathered for our morning report, the firemen arrived in their full regalia. One of the nurses asked a cute fireman if he was on a calendar! We are so bad! He gave a little smile, but kept to his task of going to the area to ensure that there was no fire present. Quite the unusual excitement for the morning!

Around two-thousand-and-fourteen, marijuana became legal to possess and smoke in the state I lived in. On several occasions now when I have gone in to interview the parents regarding their child's operation, the lingering smell of pot is evident. This is a little strange for two reasons. First, it means that the parents were smoking pot early in the morning before bringing their child to the hospital, and secondly, that the parents are driving to the hospital with their child in the car while they are under the influence. I remember one patient's mother was so stoned and unaware of her surroundings, that when it was time for me to take her child back to the OR for the child's operation, I had to instruct the mother to lift her arms up off the side rails of the crib, so that I could pull the crib with the child in it towards the OR. The mother startled, and then finally lifted her arms up off the crib!

I, as an employee of the hospital, have never been drug tested, which I think is interesting. I am not sure if drug testing is not done because of the expense of it, or all the complications that could arise from the staff being drug tested, and finding that the staff were positive for drug use; such as counseling, replacing staff if they were fired, etc. I would guess that the general public would imagine that employees of a hospital are regularly drug tested. I personally have never witnessed an employee at work that I suspected was under the influence of any kind of drug. Physicians and nurses are supposed to be at high risk for drug abuse, as they have access to many drugs. There is even a program in place at the hospital that if an employee voluntarily admits to having a drug problem, they will not be fired, but instead, will receive treatment for it.

Yesterday, I worked with my favorite urologist, Dr. G.. He is so very nice, that you always feel safe from being criticized in his room, and all the staff love to work his blocks. He had several cases that day, and we were running ahead of schedule by about thirty minutes, which had been my goal for the day. After interviewing the mom regarding the child's npo status and any potential allergies her child might have, as well as the mom's understanding of the operation her child was having, I was just about to roll out of the holding area with the child, when the mom said, "Oh, he is also having blood drawn for an allergy test while he is in the OR." My heart sank to my feet with that statement, as I had heard nothing about this blood draw from the nurse working in the pre-surgery area, who had given me report on this patient. Also, there were no blood collection tubes on the chart like there should be, if we knew that blood needed to be collected during the OR procedure. "Did you tell the pre-surgery nurse about the blood draw during the admit process?" I asked. "No," the Mom stated. "I talked to a nurse last night when they called the house, and I mentioned it to her."

The night before an operation, a nurse calls the family, and gives the parents instructions on where to come, what to bring to the OR, and when to stop giving their child food or drink. Unfortunately, mentioning a blood draw to that nurse will not trigger any mechanism where the blood draw will be accomplished the next day in the OR.

Also, the general public does not seem to understand that I, as a nurse, cannot do something like a blood draw without a physician's order, just because the parent says that their child needs it. To accomplish the blood draw, the physician needs to be contacted so that he can issue an order for the blood draw; lab specimen labels need to be printed up with instructions for me as the nurse, on which color of tubes I need to put the blood in, and how many milliliters of blood that need to be collected in each tube. In other words, it is complicated. I went back to the OR, explained the blood draw dilemma to Dr. G.; and the process of contacting the outside physician began. We spent a good extra thirty to forty minutes getting together the order, along with the tubes, so that we could accommodate this mother's request. In the future, it would be fabulous if the parents could mention any unusual requests right away to the nurse as they are being admitted.

Chapter

17

MRSA (Methicillin Resistant Staph Aureus) became a big deal a few years ago, when the bacteria began to mutate, and became resistant to different antibiotics. If we get a patient in for surgery that has previously been diagnosed with MRSA, even if their outbreak was years ago, we have to put on a cover gown and gloves before we work with that patient. To be cleared of a MRSA diagnosis, the patient has to go in for repeated tests for MRSA, that all must come up negative. Once a patient has been diagnosed with MRSA, that diagnosis tends to follow them around for the rest of their life, even if they no longer have active disease. What I think is funny, is that as medical workers we put on gowns and gloves for people with a MRSA diagnosis, but sometimes we don't gown and glove when a person has some other really nasty infection, because it is undiagnosed.

One case I can think of was an older teenage boy who had decided it was cool to pierce his own ears. He had done this many times, as he had multiple piercings in both ears. Unfortunately for him, his last piercing had not gone well, and he had gotten a terrible infection. I have never seen before or since, an ear that swollen! It was amazing to me to see how huge his ear had gotten without splitting! That ear must have been three times its normal size, and was draining a nasty whitish substance. I can only imagine how painful that ear must have been for that boy! I didn't need any prompting that day to don my gown and gloves, before I dealt with him as my patient! I don't know what he had, but it wasn't good, and I sure didn't want to get it!

Around one o'clock in the afternoon I went to pick up my patient on the medical surgical floor. The young man had a ruptured appendix, and was coming down to the OR to have it removed. The med-surg nurse was late in giving the patient his noon IV antibiotics. Since antibiotics are very important to a patient with a ruptured appendix, I waited for the nurse to get, and give his antibiotics to him before I took the patient down to the OR. Now everything is done electronically, so the med-surg nurse scanned the patient's wrist band, and then scanned the antibiotics. The patient's computer monitor screen flashed red, which I figured was not good. I moved closer to the screen to read that the antibiotics she had were not the correct dosage. The amount she had was more than the prescribed amount. Years ago, when I was a floor nurse, if you had too much medication, that was not a problem. You, as a highly educated nurse, knew how to divide and do fractions, and could figure out how much to give and how much to throw out, but the patient would have gotten their dose of antibiotics. In this case, the nurse told me that she couldn't give the antibiotic because it was too much, and that she had to return the antibiotic to the pharmacy! I was stunned! What have they reduced nurses to? In an effort to not have medication errors, I think they have gotten ridiculous! I had to take my patient to the OR without him receiving his antibiotics, because who knew how long it would take for the pharmacy to deliver the correct amount of antibiotic. Once I had taken the patient down to the OR, I told the anesthesiologist what had transpired, and that the patient still needed his noon dose of antibiotic. The anesthesiologist grabbed a vial of the correct antibiotic, and mixed it into solution herself, administered it to the patient, and the problem was solved quickly. Good thing the pharmacy can't see that! No scanning of any sort took place just like in the old days! That is another thing I loved about working in the OR.... we didn't seem to have a million rules governing and hindering us from giving good care.

Two years ago, when I gave up my staff position, which had included health benefits, I purchased an individual health policy. After one year of being insured, my policy payment went up over ten percent. I was just notified a day ago, that my health premium would go up next year to over forty percent of what it was this year! That equals a fifty percent increase in two years! The payment for my individual plan was going to be thirteen hundred dollars a month! I wish my salary as a nurse went up fifty percent every two years.

Apparently, not only is the House and the Senate not willing to tweak and streamline the Affordable Care Act to help all of us citizens who have to purchase our own private health care, but according to my health care provider; Congress has changed some federal laws which seem to be sabotaging private health care! The republican Speaker of the House even made a public speech declaring his desire for sabotaging the Affordable Care Act, since the ACA was not repealed as the Republican Party wanted it to be. How rude is that, that the people who are paid to serve the American people that have elected them are not only NOT going to help, but that they are actively engaged in sabotaging them! Persons serving in the Senate and the House of Representatives all have wonderful health care, and probably have to pay little, if anything, for their health care.

We have made some progress in health care though. I remember when not that many years ago, an individual could not even purchase an individual health plan, no matter how high the premium might be! Health insurance companies were not interested in insuring individuals, and therefore, did not provide individual policies. Also, insurance companies were allowed to discriminate against individuals who had previous health conditions, which had the potential to make the companies less profitable. Both of those situations have been rectified, which is wonderful. Now, it would be wonderful, if we could just modify the Affordable Care Act by limiting liability, and reducing the cost of pharmaceuticals.

I remember a personal experience from decades ago, when the company my husband worked for changed health insurance companies. I happened at the time to be pregnant, and the new health insurance company told my husband and I that my pregnancy was a pre-existing condition, and therefore, they would not cover my pregnancy! This situation was ridiculous, as I had been covered by the previous insurer the entire time, before the switch to the new company. After hassling the new insurer, along with the fact that my husband's father owned the company that had made the switch, my pregnancy was granted coverage.

It was my thirtieth-year anniversary working for the hospital, and they were generously giving me a gift to celebrate. The brochure showed several choices of gifts that I could choose from. The interesting thing to me was the disparity between the value of the gifts. For instance, you could choose a simple little pin that had the company logo on it, or a barbeque. Pick a leather purse, or an umbrella. Is this some kind of an IQ test? If I pick a low-cost item over a more expensive one, do I receive a mandatory intelligence test later? I settled on a beautiful black leather purse, which I enjoy very much.

She was only two years old, and had been a healthy child until last April when her mother had disappeared. She had been placed with her biological father after that, and in July he had beaten her so severely that she had suffered a traumatic brain injury, and was completely disabled. It was not known if she was blind, but she would never walk or talk again. She was with us in the OR to have a gastrostomy tube placed, so that she could be fed more easily through it, because she wasn't able to eat either. What a bad, sad, tragic case!!! Fortunately, we don't see many cases as bad as this, and yet even one child that suffers like she had, is one to many.

We proceeded to do the case laparoscopically; where small incisions were made, and no instruments needed to be counted before, or after, the surgery. Because this child had a huge liver, the surgeon in the middle of the case decided to 'go open,' which meant that because of the difficulties he was experiencing, he was now abandoning the idea of doing the surgery laparoscopically.

With an open belly case, instruments need to be counted before the operation, and then counted at the end of the operation, to ensure that no instrument is accidentally left behind. Almost everyone has heard of cases where retractors and other instruments are left accidentally inside of patients, and then the retained instrument is discovered later. The public is horrified, and wonders how could this even be possible? This case was a good example of what the staff are up against in the real world. The laparoscopic set that was being used included some instruments which were exactly identical to some of the instruments found in the major set, which we were now about to open.

The instruments in the major set, a large pan consisting of ninety-one instruments, now needed to be counted while the surgeon was still asking for instruments and supplies. The surgical-technician was also trying to separate the instruments that were already in use, from the set that was now being opened. It was quite a challenge, and in a perfect world the surgeon would stop working for five minutes, while the exchange was made and counted. Some cases use as many as ten pans all containing instruments! Also, at the end of an abdominal case, the surgeon commonly continues to ask for instruments, while the last instrument count is being conducted. Both the circulator and surgical-tech are trying to keep track of which instrument has already been counted while the instruments are still on the move! It is very difficult, and one can see how easily it would be to make a mistake while counting the many instruments, sponges, and sharps. I think that the only way to ensure that instruments are never left in a patient is if a policy is made and enforced, where the surgeon finishes the case, the instruments are regrouped in their various pans that they came in originally, and are then counted.

Also, to add to the complexity, is that sometimes the case is not going as well as one would hope. When the case is difficult, there is more tension on the surgeon's part which transmits to the surgical-tech, as well as to the other staff in the room.

In this particular case, the surgical-tech dropped a needle driver containing a needle onto the floor. The needle driver broke open, and we were scouring the floor to find the needle. If the end count is off for instruments, sponges, or sharps; which consist of needles, bovie-tips, knife blades, and hypos, and even if you know the needle landed on the floor but you cannot find it, an X-ray has to be performed on the patient to ensure that it is not inside the patient. This is not good on many levels. X-ray has to be called, an incident report has to be filled out, plus the patient receives radiation.

Needles are notorious for getting hung up in all kinds of places. The needle can stick onto the surgeon's gown as the needle is falling, or the suture can stick to gloves; especially if the gloves have a little blood on them, which makes the suture stickier. In this case, I finally found the errant needle with its clear suture on the floor, about six-inches away from where the needle driver had landed, so we were very relieved to find it.

Many hospitals are non-profit organizations. Many people think that hospitals exist only to care for the public, and are not necessarily interested in making money. Nothing could be further from the truth. Hospitals are businesses, and are interested in making a profit, just like other businesses. Hospitals compete heavily with each other. The state regulates how many hospitals can be in a certain area. If a competing hospital is already located there, the only way another hospital can build is to file a 'certificate of need' with the state, and see if the state will allow them to build.

When robotic surgery became possible, our hospital scrambled to pay millions to purchase the equipment; becoming the first hospital in the area able to offer this new service to patients, beating out the competing hospital down the street.

In nineteen-eighty-six, Congress enacted the Emergency Medical Treatment and Active Labor Act, ensuring public access to emergency services, where a person could be treated and stabilized, regardless of that person's ability to pay. It is a federal statute that governs when and how a patient may be one; refused treatment, or two; transferred from one hospital to another when the patient is in an unstable medical condition. It was designed to prevent hospitals from transferring uninsured or Medicaid patients to public hospitals, without at least first providing a medical screening examination to ensure that the patient was stable for transfer. Since its enactment in nineteen-eighty-six, it has remained unfunded by the government. In other words, any treatment provided by the hospital's ER goes unpaid, if the patient does not have any medical insurance, or is paid very little, if the insurer has poor compensation, such as Medicaid.

As an example, one case that I remember was when a two-year-old boy was sent to our hospital in the middle of the night for an emergent case, because the local hospital didn't want to treat him. The boy had children's state welfare health insurance, which typically paid a very low reimbursement to the hospital. The boy lived two hours away from our hospital, and even though his case was emergent, the other local hospital refused to treat him, and they sent him up north to us. The local hospital would say in their defense, that the boy would receive better care at our children's hospital, but we think it was because the hospital didn't like the low reimbursement. This case, which was a testicular torsion, was an emergency, and yet they made the patient drive for over two hours to reach our hospital! Our surgeon and the anesthesiologist were so mad over this incident, that they decided to call the doctors from the other hospital in the middle of the night to give them an update on how their patient was doing, waking up both of them!

Other issues with compensation were becoming a problem for some of the surgeons that I worked with, who still had independent practices. One pediatric surgeon told me that the mother of one of his patients had brought him a copy of the bill she had received from our hospital for her seven-year-old son who had a surgical circumcision performed by that surgeon. The bill from the hospital was twenty-three thousand dollars, while the surgeon was to receive two-hundred and twenty dollars for his services! That infuriated the surgeon to no end; that his fees were being squeezed into oblivion, and yet without him, the hospital wouldn't be able to charge those outrageous amounts.

Another thing that same surgeon had noticed recently was that a divorced couple would bring their child in for a surgery consultation. The father had health insurance through the Affordable Care Act (aka Obamacare), and was providing the health insurance for the child which would pay the surgeon two-hundred dollars for the circumcision surgery on his older child. The surgery would be scheduled, but because the father's insurance required a copayment of about six-thousand dollars, the dad, before the surgery was performed, would knowingly switch the child over to the mom's healthcare which was Medicaid; which only would pay the surgeon about eighty dollars for the surgery. For the fee of eighty dollars, the surgeon was actually losing money to perform the thirty to forty-minute surgery, when he factored in his office costs, so the surgeon was considering refusing to perform circumcisions any more. The surgeon said he was seeing a high rate of patients that were knowingly practicing this switch on him!

I had a patient last week, that weighed four-hundred and ninety-six pounds. He was the same age as I was, and I felt great distress at seeing what terrible shape he was in. He was bed-bound. When you weigh that much all of your systems are on the brink of failure. Hypertension, diabetes, you name it; and he had it. His legs had terrible blood perfusion, and were leathery and dark. He was there because he had started throwing up blood. We had a very difficult time moving him from the medical surgical floor down to the OR, because of the extra-large width of the hospital bed he was lying in. With a lot of help from other staff, we were finally able to get him into the OR to have an endoscopy. The patient was anesthetized, and a scope was placed down his esophagus to determine where the bleeding was coming from. It turned out that he had a tear in his esophagus, which was the cause of his immediate problem. Knowing now what the problem was, his gastroenterologist could come up with a treatment plan for him. I certainly wish him well.

Chapter
18

Yesterday, we worked on a case involving a cataract removal from a child's eye, along with replacing the damaged lens with an artificial one. The child was two-years old, and he had recently had a cataract removed from his other eye. Cataracts can occur congenitally, which means children can be born with them. Many people think that only older people have cataracts, but this is not true. We also sometimes see a child with a cataract in only one eye which was caused by an injury.

Our patient was given eye drops before the surgery, which dilated the pupil of his eye. This allowed the surgeon to see the damaged lens easily. A small incision was made in the eye, and a special phaco tip was inserted into the eye which emulsified the damaged lens. Next, the bits of emulsified lens were vacuumed out. A new artificial lens was folded over and placed through the tiny incision into the eye. Once inside the eye, the lens unfolded on its own, and after being happy with the placement of the lens, the surgeon closed the incision with the tiniest suture and needle you have ever seen. The surgery takes about thirty minutes to complete. Antibiotic and numbing eye drops were placed in the affected eye, and then an eye patch was placed over the eye. Sometimes, we have had problems using our phaco machine while doing cases. For example, one time the software for the machine had been updated without any notification to the staff who use it. One set of tubing would work in it, while another set of tubing that looked identical to the naked eye, would not be recognized by the computer, and would not work! Of course, as luck would have it, we put the wrong set of tubing in first, and could not figure out why it wouldn't work. We decided in frustration to try another set of tubing which luckily happened to be the one recognized by the new software, and yet we still had no idea at the time why that tubing worked, when the other tubing didn't. We found out about the software update later.

Another time, I happened to be scrubbing for Dr. S. as we did a cataract removal and lens replacement. During the case the surgeon could not get the phaco machine to work properly. In frustration, he turned to me and said, "This child is going to lose his eye!" What a horrible thought! There was no way we were going to let that happen! "Let me think," I replied. We tried a few different things, and the phaco began to work properly. The surgery was a success. Later, weeks after the case was done, we found out that the foot pedal that operates the phaco machine had been replaced with a new one that would perform different functions depending on where you put pressure on the foot pedal! Who knew?

Today I was helping in the main OR, and another nurse had a large bowel case she needed help with. The first thing that was asked of me was to help count all the instruments with the scrub-tech before the case began, which I did. The poor patient had recently had a colostomy, and it had become abscessed. The room had the most terrible smell of rotting flesh and bowel contents. The team working that case begged for me to go get some peppermint oil, so I could dab it onto their masks to help them mask the smell in the room. We have peppermint oil available in 'the core.' The core is a long corridor filled with supplies that all of the OR rooms have their back-door face.

I remember a bowel case years ago, that had that same terrible smell. The surgeon had actually pulled out the man's bowels, and had them draped all over a back table. Both the surgeon and the anesthesiologist told me that the patient would pass away that night, but yet the surgeon had to perform the operation as if the man would survive. I felt so sorry for the patient. I also felt sorry for the surgeon, who would be spending hours on this operation knowing it was all for naught.

Yesterday, we had a mom who insisted that she would be going back to the OR to help her child while he was being anesthetized. She had said nothing about this to the surgeon when he talked to her, but she did tell the anesthesiologist in no uncertain terms that she would be coming back with her child. I asked the anesthesiologist if we were cancelling the case, as it is our policy not to allow parents back into the OR.

There are several reasons for this policy, all dealing with safety and cleanliness. First, special attire is used in the OR to keep it clean. Scrubs are worn by the staff, and hair is covered with a shower-like cap. Shoes dedicated for wearing only in the OR are kept in the staff lockers, so they are not used outside of the OR. To allow a parent to come back to the OR with their child, would mean that time would have to be taken to help the parent dress in coveralls to cover their street clothes, provide them with shoe covers, a hat to cover their hair, and help them tie on a mask.

Secondly, children go through a phase of anesthesia called stage-two, where the unconscious child appears to struggle, which could freak out an uninformed parent. Also, what happens if the parent decides to faint in the OR....and the staff is busy with the child? Who is going to help the parent who has fainted? What happens if the parent injures themself by hitting something as they faint? It is not uncommon for nursing students to feel faint in the OR. What if the parent becomes hysterical seeing their child go through stage-two of anesthesia? We as staff, would like to avoid having to deal with any of these possible situations. Also, who will escort the parent back out to the waiting area once their child is anesthetized? We usually don't have extra staff to help the parents. For all of these reasons, our hospital has the policy that the child goes back into the OR without the parents.

Occasionally, parents will threaten the anesthesiologist that if anything happens to their child they will "hunt them down!" Most anesthesiologists take this statement in stride, but some anesthesiologists will cancel the case anytime a parent threatens them.

In this particular case, the surgeon was informed of mom's demands, and he went in to talk with her, and told her that she had one of two choices--the child could have the operation without her there, or she could take her child home without the operation. She chose to let the child come back without her, but she was extremely upset with all of us, because she did not get her wish. Because hospitals are run as businesses, we see more and more that patients act as consumers.... as if they were ordering a meal, and they want it a certain way; instead of realizing that we are educated professionals, and we have reasons for everything we do.

Can you imagine a passenger on an airplane going up to the cockpit, and demanding the pilot to fly the plane a certain way? From what I have heard, some hospitals are even having patient satisfaction drive the surgeon's salaries! If we were making cheeseburgers that would be one thing, but how can a physician get high patient satisfaction scores if he or she tells their patient that they are overweight, or need to give up smoking immediately? Medical people have the responsibility of telling their patient what is in the patient's best interest, which may not always make the patient happy.

Dr. S., the eye surgeon, was asked by the hospital if he would like to join an 'NAT' team that was being formed. NAT stands for non-accidental trauma, or in layman's term--child abuse. When a child is admitted to the hospital and child abuse is suspected, X-rays are performed to look for fresh or old fractures of the child's bones. An eye surgeon also performs an eye exam, in which he can see damage inside the eye, if the baby was shaken violently. While Dr. S. is very benevolent, and loves to help children in particular, he declined the offer for purely economic reasons. If he examined the child, and the case for abuse went to court, Dr. S. would be asked to testify, and he would have to spend the day in court waiting to testify. For that service he would receive a twelve-dollar witness fee. Dr. S. was one of the few surgeons I worked with who still was not an employee of the hospital. His costs to run his independent office, pay all of his employees and their health benefits, along with his costs for his liability insurance, building costs, etc. for that day are astronomically higher than the twelve dollars he would receive for being a witness, so he had to regretfully decline joining the NAT team.

Over the years, I have only had one patient die while in the

OR, and that was a small infant. As I looked at the baby lying on the OR table before we even began his operation, the baby looked so sick, that I had the unusual thought that he might not live. I had never had that thought with any of my patients, before or since. Before we could even really get started and were just intubating him, he passed away. Usually, it is much more difficult for young children to die, as all their tissue is new and relatively healthy, especially their heart. Adults, on the other hand, have many body parts that are just plain worn out from years of use.

The anesthesiologist asked me to call a code, and the surgeon began compressions. Usually in the OR, the staff is directed to call an internal code only, not a code that is broadcast over the entire hospital. However, it was the weekend, and we had a very limited staff presence in the OR area. I decided if it was my baby, I would want everyone I could get in attendance to that code, even if it meant upsetting the parents in the waiting room, as they would hear the code called overhead. I told the secretary to call an external code blue, and soon the room was filled with people ready and able to help. Unfortunately, the baby never recovered. We swaddled him up nicely in blankets, so he could be taken back to his grieving parents for them to be able to hold him, and to say goodbye. This baby had been in the unfortunate situation of having a bowel obstruction that would kill him without an operation, and yet he had become so septic from having an obstructed bowel, that he died anyway. I wondered for a long time afterward, if something could have been done differently to enable him to survive, but I could think of nothing different that we could have done for him.

I have had a few other patients that went on to die after

leaving the OR. One was a teenage girl that told me in the interview that she would not survive the operation. As an OR nurse, you are taught to take this kind of information seriously, so I passed it onto the anesthesiologist. I can't remember at this time what her surgery was, except that it was deemed essential, so the decision was made to proceed. As soon as she was intubated, the anesthesiologist noticed that he was having a hard time ventilating her. This was strange, as she was young and a non-smoker; she should have been very easy to ventilate. All through the operation the anesthesiologist struggled with keeping her ventilated. After the operation was done, she went to the PICU where it was discovered that she had undiagnosed lung cancer, and she never recovered. This was quite shocking to all of us as she was so young, and that she had been correct in her prophesy of not surviving.

One morning I came into work, and after I got there realized that I didn't feel that well. I informed the charge nurse that I thought I was starting to feel ill, and she said to just keep her informed if I needed to go home. I was assigned that day to scrub for a crusty old ENT surgeon that I knew well. I scrubbed two cases that morning and was doing okay, until we had a little lag time before the next patient was brought into the room and I sat down, waiting for the patient to arrive. When I stood up, I could tell that I was going to pass out if I didn't put my head between my legs, so I excused myself, left the OR room, and sat down with my head between my legs. I could see the charge nurse down the hall, so I yelled to her, but she never acted like she could hear me at all. In the OR if anyone starts yelling, you get an immediate response; as everyone assume you are having some kind of emergency. I was surprised that no one was responding to me! Apparently, my yelling was in reality only a whisper, and that is why no one was coming to help me! Another scrub was found to replace me, and help the surgeon with the rest of his cases. I lay down for a while and drank a pop, before going home to recover. Several days later, the same surgeon told me that I had looked 'as white as a ghost,' when I left his room that day!

Surgeon's pagers are another thing that can drive a circulator completely bonkers! Before the surgery begins, the surgeon usually places their pager on the back counter of the OR room, but sometimes they forget to, and when their pager goes off you have to dig it out of their pockets while they are scrubbed in on a case! After the pager goes off, the surgeon always wants to know who called, and usually they want you to call the person back, to find out what they called about.

One pediatric general surgeon that I worked with frequently was Dr. H. When he was on-call as the designated trauma surgeon for the day, his pager would go off continually. As the circulator you have your own work you need to do, and it really annoyed me if his pager went off constantly. You become in essence, a personal secretary to the surgeon! One day, Dr. H.'s pager went off, and he asked me to call the emergency room who had paged him; which I did. I had learned from previous experience to always keep the person I called on the phone, while I relayed the message to the surgeon. In this case, it was about another child that had come into the ER, that the ER physician wanted Dr. H. to consult on. Dr. H. became stressed out, and started yelling at me, "I am already in surgery, what do you expect me to do?" At this, I became angry and very quiet. The ER physician on the phone, overhearing Dr. H.'s comment, said he would talk to Dr. H.

later. Our case continued on, and after a while Dr. H.'s pager went off again. This time I didn't make any move to answer it. After a few minutes, Dr. H. said, "I think my pager went off." I replied, "Yes, it did." Another minute went by.

Dr. H. said, "Could you see who is calling please?" I thought to myself, who else would it be, but the ER? I looked at his pager and answered, "It is the ER." Another minute went by and Dr. H. asked, "Could you please call them, and find out what they want?" I did, but I think Dr. H. got the message.

Another time, an adult patient had come in with a huge basketball-sized benign tumor growing in her abdomen, and three different surgeons were in on that case, because it was so interesting. All three of their pagers were lying on the back counter, and constantly going off! Meanwhile, I was busy documenting the specimen so it could be labeled and processed. Talk about adding stress, and being annoying! Those three pagers going off were enough to make me completely crazy!

Chapter
19

Several years ago, our hospital converted from paper charting to electronic charting. This I believe, was due to a federal mandate. The idea behind it was that when a patient went to a physician or a hospital, that any facility would be able to see the patient's past interactions and history. That was a great idea, but unfortunately the federal mandate apparently did not include that all the different electronic charting systems used by different hospitals and clinics needed to be interfaced with each other!

As one can imagine, this new program has led to a lot of adaptation pains. One morning, I was working with the eye surgeon, Dr S., and I told him that I was unable to locate his electronic history and physical (H&P) for one of his patients. As a circulator, I need to have a history and physical that relates to the operation that is taking place that day, and it also has to be dated within thirty days of the operation that is taking place. The H&P also must address all of the patient's major organs, such as heart, lungs, etc. At this point in time the 'upgrade' which added the electronic H&P was about two weeks old. If you ever want to see a surgeon's blood pressure rise quickly, just mention to them some problem you are having finding their H&P!

Dr. S. unloaded on me with all of his frustrations and problems with the recent 'upgrade', converting the H&P from paper to now being electronic. Dr. S. told me that I could just cancel that patient's case since I didn't have a history and physical; and that I would be the person to tell the family that their case was cancelled, since they had driven a long distance that morning to have their child's operation!

I could see that I needed to get a tech-support person to help him get the program to work correctly for him, but I couldn't put that into motion until I let him finish venting. We have worked together for years, so I knew that he would calm down eventually, and we would get the problem solved. After several phone calls to management to ask for help in my predicament, and after being told by an admitting nurse and a new resident nurse that a paper letter from a physician about this case was the same as a history and physical (which it isn't), I decided to just let the case go on, even though I did not have all the pieces I technically needed. I knew from my past history with Dr. S. that he always had his history and physicals completed meticulously, and that his H&P would appear in the electronic charting at some point in time. Disaster was averted yet once again!

A few weeks ago, besides now having an electronic history and physical (H&P), another part of the new electronic charting was put into action, and that was an electronic consent. On the consent, the patient's medical condition and the operation to be performed are typed into the computer, and then the nurse and the patient, or in the case of a child, the patient's parent, signs on a signature pad, which is recorded electronically. The physician as well, needs to sign the consent via the signature pad; and since many of the physicians do not have the same electronic charting system at their office, along with the signature pad, they must sign the consent in the OR.

When the electronic consent first came out, Dr. S. and I had a similar problem. Before one case began, Dr. S. had decided that he needed to work on both eyes, instead of just the one eye. Before the advent of going electronic, we used a simple paper consent. With a paper consent, I would have gone over the change in the consent with the parents, and simply added the other eye to the consent with both of us initialing our approval, and that would be that. Instead, once the electronic consent was signed, there was no changing it! A whole new consent needed to be filled out electronically, and signed again by all the parties. I used to be a stickler on consents being absolutely correct, but the electronic version has loosened me up. There is a statement in the consent that allows the surgeon to do whatever he deems necessary during the operation, so I try my best to get the consent to be perfect, but if that is not possible, and in my judgement I think the situation requires it, I go ahead with that clause in mind.

One of my cases today, was a little boy that was going to have a circumcision revision. He was three years old, and I had noticed on one of our schedules in the OR that someone had hand written in the words ph-probe next to his surgery. I asked the surgeon about it when we were finishing up with the case before the circumcision revision. The surgeon said that he remembered something about it, but wasn't sure of any of the details. It turned out that this little boy had a history of reflux, and the doctors in the GI clinic wanted a ph-probe placed at the same time he was having surgery.

Having two procedures done by two different surgeons really complicates things. First of all, is the gastroenterologist available to place the probe at the same time as the other surgeon, who is revising the circumcision? Do we have a consent for the second procedure? If not, all of those things can slow down the speed at which we can continue on with our block of surgeries.

As it turned out, there was no consent for the ph-probe, although some of the pre-surg nurses said a consent wasn't needed for that procedure! After several phone calls, I also found out that the GI physician was not available during our surgery time-frame.

To accommodate the parents, the anesthesiologist decided that she would place the ph-probe in the OR. This was very nice of her because by doing so, she took on some added liability if anything should go wrong with the placement. It would have been very easy for her to tell the parents, "I'm sorry, but your GI physician is not available, so you will have to make other arrangements." Consent was given, and the anesthesiologist acquired the probe and placed it, before we began the regularly scheduled surgery of the circumcision revision, but the whole process of looking into the availability of the GI physician, and acquiring the probe added about a forty-minute delay. This is one of the reasons that surgeries do not always start at their scheduled time. The other common one, is that the surgeon can run into complications during surgery, and it takes longer to finish the surgery then it was scheduled for.

We were having a good morning working with Dr. S. His cases required two circulators, as some of the procedures such as tear-duct probes were very quick (about three minutes long). I was the nurse on the computer, and a fairly new nurse was doing patient care. For each case, the consent needed to be electronically signed before the patient was brought back into the room. Tamara, the other nurse, had finished her residency in the OR almost a year ago, and was well aware of this policy.

I, as the nurse working on the computer, gave Tamara a heads-up that the consent on a particular patient had not been signed by the parents, or the surgeon yet. Usually, the consents are signed in pre-surgery before the patient comes to us. It is one of the duties that the admitting nurses have, but sometimes it gets missed, and so it is still part of the circulator's job to make sure that you have a signed, correct consent.

If the consent has not been signed previously, we have an electronic signature pad next to the holding room, where we interview the child's parents before surgery. We can pull up the electronic chart, go over the consent with the parents, and then have them sign the consent. The surgeon has an electronic signature pad available at the computer they sit and chart at, so the surgeon can sign independently from the parents. No big deal.

On our very last case, I heard Tamara coming down the hall with the child, and I went out and told her that the consent still had not been signed. The anesthesiologist became very irritated with me, and told me that I should have taken care of this, because I had worked there forever; and that Tamara was only a resident nurse. I retorted that she was not a resident nurse anymore, at which he went to Tamara and held up the security badge she was wearing, which identified her as a resident. I told the anesthesiologist once again that Tamara was not a resident anymore. She had completed the residency and was now staff. I went on to tell him that Tamara had been told that the consent was not signed, and that she had just made a simple mistake. Tamara was standing there next to me during this whole confrontation I was having with the anesthesiologist.

I kept expecting Tamara to speak up, and tell the anesthesiologist that she was not a resident anymore, that it was her mistake, she knew the procedure and had just forgotten, but instead, all she said was, "I need to get a new badge!"

The anesthesiologist still stated that it was my fault. I told the anesthesiologist, "if you want to get mad at someone how about the surgeon? He knows the procedure, and he hasn't signed his consent, has he?" At that, I walked down the hall in search of Dr. S. and finding him in the pre-surg area, I told him, "I just took a lot of heat from the anesthesiologist for you because you didn't sign your consent." He said, "I know, I'm in trouble!" He is funny! It is almost like working with your husband!

Surgeons in the OR frequently use headlights that sit on their heads during surgery. Until a couple of years ago, the only headlights we used, needed electricity to work. Now, we use very nice headlights that operate on rechargeable batteries. The older headlights had a long electrical cord that had a three-inch steel shaft on the end that plugged into an electric light box. In back cases, and other surgeries, the surgeon frequently switches sides while he operates, and so the circulator has to unplug the cord, follow the surgeon to the other side of the OR table while hanging onto the cord, and then re-plug the cord into a light box on that side. The steel shaft on the end of the cord that fits into the electrical box becomes very hot after a few minutes.

At the beginning of the case, the surgeon usually has the electrical cord stuffed into one of his back scrub pockets that is located right over his buttocks, so that the cord doesn't drag around on the floor as he walks. One of the newer circulators that had just graduated from a residency was telling me her funny story. After the surgeon had been working with his headlight plugged in for a while, he decided to move to the other side of the OR table. Instead of hanging on to the cord, the new circulator, without knowing how hot the steel shaft gets after being plugged in, decided to put the cord with the steel shaft back into the surgeon's back pocket!

Within seconds, the surgeon was screaming, "It's burning me!" Horrified, the circulator offered to check out the surgeon's burned area which would mean he would have to drop his pants! The surgeon, who happened to be, shall we say, not the easiest going of surgeons, was furious! "No, don't touch me!" he fumed.

I thought it was a very funny story. I do hope the surgeon didn't suffer a serious burn!

My last surgical case of the day was a darling six-year-old girl, who was having her crossed eyes uncrossed. She was nervous and wary of me, as I interviewed and explained to her parents where they would go while she was having surgery, and how they would get back together.

I learned several years ago, that people in general believe whatever they want to, whether things are true or not. To ease their distress and fears of leaving their parents, and coming back to the OR with me, I started telling little girls that I had a princess bed for them to lie on in the OR. The princess bed had a princess pillow, and that I had princess stickers for them as well. Of course, in reality the princess bed was the OR bed, the princess pillow was really a foam donut to lay your head on, and the princess stickers were EKG and oxygen saturation stickers, but the patient and the parents would get excited over the idea of a fun bed with stickers. For boys, I used the theme of a Ninja warrior, or super heroes.

This little girl, who had been so fearful, got on the OR table, and as we placed all her 'princess' stickers on her, gave me a big smile and stated, "This is almost fun!" She was darling.

I was doing my usual block with Dr. S., the eye surgeon. He stated "You'll be really pleased with me because one of the patients here today wanted a lot of blood drawn for tests while we were in the OR, but I told them we couldn't do it in the interest of time." I replied, "Oh, thank heavens! I get stressed out just thinking about blood draws in the OR!" Just then Lisa, another nurse who worked frequently in the OR, came in to give us report on our next patient, and plunked down a bag filled with empty glass tubes for blood collection! Dr. S. and I looked at each other in disbelief. I had been working the computer that morning, so I told the other RN who had been circulating, that when we brought in the next patient she could start an IV for the surgery procedure in the patient's hand, and that I would start an IV in the foot to try and get enough blood for the lab draws.

The patient was brought into the OR, and put to sleep with a mask filled with sevoflurane. When I looked at the patient's right ankle, she had a beautiful saphenous vein. I told the other circulator to hold off on starting her IV, because we might be able to get blood for the lab draws, and use the same site for the IV. I sunk the IV catheter into her vein, and it drew beautifully--even I was completely amazed at how I could get any amount of blood I needed effortlessly! The lab tubes were all filled, we hooked up the IV tubing, and the whole procedure only took a few extra minutes of time. I told Dr. S. "That was the most amazing blood draw I have ever been involved with!"

It is the policy of our hospital to not accept any sterile instruments or medications from outside our medical facility. The reason for not accepting sterile instruments is simple: Our processors for sterilizing equipment are checked on a daily basis. Any instruments brought in from the outside have been processed without the hospital's being able to monitor whether it has been done correctly or not.

One afternoon, we had one more quick case to do at the pediatric day surgery. The case was to be done by a plastic surgeon we didn't work with very often. Dr. W. was running about thirty minutes late when he dashed in, threw down a peel-packed instrument set and some medication, and looked at me and said, "Don't give me a hard time."

I went into another room to call my charge nurse, and I explained the situation. She agreed with me that we were unable to use the instruments he had brought with him. We do have a flash sterilizer that we could re-sterilize his instruments in, which would allow him to use those instruments, but the sterilizing process takes over fifteen minutes. Dr. W. was in a hurry to get back to his office. When I explained our options, he blew up, and started to have a fit. The anesthesiologist, who had been sitting with me while waiting for Dr. W. to show up, and who had heard all the initial conversation, started to verbally get into it with Dr. W.! This was most unusual, as most anesthesiologists never get involved in any kind of 'disagreement' a circulator might have with a surgeon. I think it has to do with the brotherhood of physicians. Now, the two doctors were having it out, and I rather enjoyed it! In the end, my director of nursing got involved and after much discussion, they decided to let Dr. W. use both his instruments and his medication, and we finished his case.

Chapter
20

Yesterday, after finishing the morning block with Dr. R., I was asked to scrub a case with an orthopedic surgeon that I used to work with as a circulator years ago. A five-year-old girl had put a very tight rubber band over her right wrist where it had stayed on all night, cutting off the circulation to her hand! In the morning, her parents were horrified when they saw her swollen purplish-red hand, and had brought her into the emergency room.

The surgeon was performing a fasciotomy, where he made three linear cuts along the side of her hand to relieve the pressure and get circulation back into it. When he came into the room and saw me as his scrub, he wasn't too happy. He is generally a grouchy person, so I didn't take it too personally. As we began the procedure, he accidentally poked me with the bovie-tip. He said, "If you don't keep out of my way, we are not going to get along." Just then, his physician's assistant came in, and she asked if he would like her to scrub in. "Yes, please!" he said emphatically. She scrubbed in, and we finished the case. You could actually see some of the purplish red color of the little girl's swollen hand turning back to a normal skin tone as we were finishing. The hand was bandaged and after her hand heals, the surgeon will sew all the open incisions back together.

Right after that case, the charge nurse asked me if I would be willing to stay late and scrub another case with a pediatric surgeon. I asked what the case was, because that charge has been notorious in the past for putting me in cases I don't feel comfortable in scrubbing. She told me it was a little mass they were taking off. I can scrub what I call 'dinky-doo' cases. All of my training for scrubbing was on the job, meaning I never got any formal training. I also don't get many opportunities to scrub, so it is harder for me to keep up my skills as a scrub nurse.

After opening the surgical drapes, towels and instruments, I overheard the circulator talking about obtaining a type and cross for blood from the patient. "Why would we need that for a simple mass removal?" I asked. "We are removing a hemangioma, not a simple mass," was the reply. Here we go again........I thought. We could be here for hours if this doesn't go well.

As the case got underway the pediatric surgeon, who I also used to work with a lot, was the complete opposite of the last surgeon. He was so happy to see me, and wondered how I had been. Fortunately for all of us, including the patient, the case went very smoothly, and we finished up. One of the new circulators told me that she had no idea that I could scrub on a case like that. I thought it was funny how differently the first surgeon reacted to me as his scrub, versus the second surgeon. I have found that it is not what you know how to do in a case, but who knows you. If the surgeon knows and likes you, you have it made!

Most of the public would assume that physicians including the anesthesiologists, would have some of the best health care insurance possible. I was talking with one of the anesthesiologists, and he told me that he paid fourteen hundred dollars a month for his health care premiums, and that he had a ten-thousand-dollar deductible! This is due in part to the fact that his anesthesia group is independent of the hospital, and so because they have less than one hundred employees, they cannot secure more favorable rates from the health insurance carriers.

Yesterday, I was working with an ENT surgeon I don't usually work with. He was very nice, and was telling us about a patient's family that came into his office complaining about their hospital bill. Their son had had his adenoids taken out by this surgeon, and the bill for the operation from the hospital was seventeen thousand dollars! The family's health insurance paid twelve thousand dollars, leaving them with five thousand dollars to pay! The family had come in to complain to the surgeon about the ridiculously high cost of their son's surgery. The surgeon told the family that the fee he received for that surgery was two hundred dollars! The family was astounded at that information.

Sometimes the thought of health care in this country, or I should say the lack of health care, drives me to distraction! My friend has a daughter, who has the unfortunate circumstance of having Crohn's disease. She occasionally develops strictures in her intestines which obstructs them, causing her severe pain. Because she has a low-paying job which does not offer medical insurance, she has Medicaid insurance. No medical facility wants to treat her because of the low monetary compensation they would receive from the state. The facility would actually be losing money if they did treat her.

Each time she becomes severely ill, she goes to the emergency room where the hospital tries to patch her up enough to get her out the door quickly, so they don't lose too much money; and thus she never receives the medical attention she would get if she had great medical insurance. After many months of being ill, and several visits to the emergency room, a surgeon finally had compassion on her plight, and performed the surgery on her that she had needed all along. That surgery relieved her obstruction on that occasion, but her condition is chronic, and she will need more surgeries down the road.

I have other friends who are older, and who are on Medicare, along with a Medicare supplement. They were just notified by letter, that their family physician could no longer see them as patients, because of the too-low compensation he would receive from the government for their care.

I remember many years ago, my mother-in-law's family doctor could not afford to see my mother-in-law when she needed her annual flu shot! The physician was limited by Medicare to charging only twenty dollars for her to come in and get her flu shot. His office costs for a person to visit were more than twenty dollars, so he quit providing that service.

Yet we spend billions of dollars on wars each year! I just don't understand why something cannot be done about this situation, when other countries have found solutions. I know; the argument is that the other country's health care is not as good as ours. That may be true for the American people that are lucky enough to have a great job with good health insurance. That argument doesn't hold true for the millions of uninsured Americans, or older Americans on Medicare. Even people with great health insurance at the present will also become old someday, or they could become critically ill for a long period of time, and find themselves unable to work, with the resulting loss of their jobs, along with the resulting loss of their health insurance. Then they would find themselves in the same situation. Who does the bell toll for?

We should realize that we are all in this together. My friend's daughter, as well as other uninsured people who visit the emergency room frequently, add to the cost of everyone else's health care premiums. Each time they are treated, the hospital takes a loss. Hospitals are businesses. They pass that loss on by charging higher fees for their services given to those of us who do have health insurance.

One week, I was working with Jeannie, who had graduated from her OR residency about a year ago. She is a hard worker, very pleasant, and a joy to work with. Jeannie and I were working Dr R.'s ENT block. To gain experience, nursing residents are paired up with experienced circulators. We had a new nurse resident working along with us, and as I was doing patient care, the resident was working with me. At work meetings, we have taken classes about what different generations value, and how the various age groups 'see' things. Since this resident was a 'millennial,' I knew that millennials only liked to be praised, and not criticized at all. I told her my little tips about how to start an IV, as well as what I said during my interview with the parents before bringing the child back for surgery. The resident had just graduated from nursing school, and had no previous experience being a nurse.

We had one patient that was about eleven years old, and was completely out of control! I brought the patient into the OR on her stretcher, but I decided that I didn't want the new resident on the receiving end of the OR table, so I had her switch positions with me, and I got the patient on the OR table without incident. I explained later to the resident that patients have been known to fall off of the OR table during transfers when inexperienced people were helping to move the patient. I also explained to her that I have seen a child jump from the stretcher in an effort to hurdle over the OR table attempting to escape out of the OR.

I don't know if she was offended, but two days later she was assigned to work with Jeannie instead of me. That day, we had a sixteen-year-old girl coming to the OR to have her tonsils removed. I was the 'facilitator' that day, and my job was to pick up patients from pre-surgery and bring them down to the holding room where the surgeon, anesthesiologist, and circulator could interview them. I went to pick up the next patient from the pre-surgical area, and the girl had a metal lip-ring and two metal earrings still on! She also had a boyfriend in the room. I explained to the mother that we would like to have all of her metal jewelry removed from her, as we were going to use cautery. I also told the new nurse working in the pre-surgery area that morning, that it would have been nice if the girl's metal jewelry had all been removed before I came to get her to take her back for surgery.

The pre-surgery nurse was very apologetic, and everything was removed except for one earring, which would not come out without extraordinary measures. We padded and taped the earring before surgery, and her ear was fine after surgery. I have never personally seen a patient burned at the site of any jewelry that the patient was unable to remove, but because it still could potentially happen; we, as circulators, are so much happier when all metal jewelry has been removed from our patients prior to them coming back to the OR!

Last week I was teaching a new nurse some of my IV tips and techniques. My first tip is to take the time to look all over the patient until you see a vein that you are fairly confident that you can successfully access. Sometimes, especially on a chubby baby, you may not be able to find a vein, but I think most new nurses do not spend enough time looking for the best vein available to them. My second tip, is that I like to put the tourniquet on at the last minute, just before starting the IV.

When you put the tourniquet on, the veins all plump up nicely. After a short time, the veins start to shrink back to their normal size. I also explain to new nurses that veins run parallel to the surface of the skin. New nurses tend to plunge the IV catheter in too deeply, and go right through the vein.

Sometimes when you are starting an IV, and you get into the vein, you are unable to advance the catheter easily. Your overwhelming urge is to shove the catheter in to make it go in which never, in my experience, works. Instead, as I explained to this new nurse, if you are unable to advance the catheter easily, stop; use a tourniquet, or your hand as a tourniquet on the patient's arm, and pull the catheter back until blood can be seen flowing again into your IV catheter. Then connect the IV tubing and turn on the IV fluid. Once the fluid is running in, wait three or four seconds, and then see if you can gently advance the IV catheter all the way into the vein. This is called 'floating in the IV.' This technique usually works about sixty to seventy percent of the time for me. In the past, I have had many anesthesiologists tell me that there is no way I am going to be successful in floating in my IV, only to watch me do it.

Apparently, the anesthesiologist who was working with us that morning had been listening several weeks ago, as I had explained the same technique to another nurse; and was eager to tell me that he too, had started an IV in the last few days when he had encountered this same problem of not having the catheter advance easily. His face was beaming, as he told me that he had used my technique with success, and how surprised he was that it actually worked!

In the hallway I ran into the eye surgeon, Dr. S., who I work with frequently. He asked me if I was excited about the upcoming solar eclipse that would be happening the next week. Admitting I was unaware of the event, he was surprised and made a joke of how well informed I was of current events. He offered me a pair of special eyeglasses so I could watch the eclipse without damaging my eyes. I replied that I wasn't going to be in Washington State, as we were leaving on the day of the eclipse to travel to Utah by airplane. As soon as I had said those words, I realized my mistake, along with seeing the shocked look on his face. I laughed, as I admitted that I realized a solar eclipse would also be taking place in other states, as well as the one I lived in. He said "Here, take these glasses. I wouldn't want your eyesight to deteriorate any more than it already has, for when you help me scrub my cases!"

Now, I was shocked at his comment. He laughed heartily, and told me that he was only joking, and that he only teases the people he likes the most!

Staff sometimes becomes ill on the job, which can lead to some interesting situations. Surgeons and anesthesiologists rarely call in sick, because they hate to have their cases canceled, knowing how hard this can be on their patients. I have seen surgeons literally brought to their knees with illness, and have to sit down in a corner of the operating room to rest. All the rules go out the window when someone is ill. Juice or pop is brought to the ailing person in an effort to revive them. Usually food and drink are strictly forbidden in the operating room. One time, I looked over to see the surgical-tech go down, and no one else noticed right away. I called for help, and the rest of the staff jumped into action. The ailing person is attended to, and another person is quickly found to replace them, and the operation continues to hum along.

I was scrubbing with Dr. S. the other morning, and I wanted to ask him a personal question. This would be the perfect time to do it, as I could quietly ask him my question without the other people in the room overhearing our conversation. My situation was this: In the last several months I had experienced two episodes where I was staring at a computer and my vision just went out! I could still see some things, but I could no longer read words, and there was a shimmery, wavy light where the computer screen was! No pain was associated with my vision loss. I was quite frightened when it first happened. I wondered if I was having a stroke, or what was going on.

The episodes usually lasted about fifteen or twenty minutes, and then all of a sudden, I was able to see again clearly! Weird! I thought Dr. S. as an eye surgeon, would be the perfect person to ask. I am sure that most physicians cringe whenever they hear the words from someone: "I want to ask you about a weird thing I experienced......"

Anyway, I brought up the subject to Dr. S. He stopped and looked at me. He said, "Have you been using drugs lately?" "No, I exclaimed." He replied, "You can be honest with me." "I am being honest with you," I protested. He laughed, and said that what I was having was a visual migraine. I had never heard of it before. He said the experts are not sure what causes it, but that they are fairly common, and that he himself experienced them frequently. He later gave me a print-out on visual migraines, and the literature described almost exactly what I was experiencing. It was great to find out that I was still halfway normal!

One time, I was called in very late at night, for a case. Our case was a child with a broken arm. Broken limbs sometimes are so bad that they require the surgeon to open the limb up in order to repair the bone fracture with plates and screws. Those cases are referred to as ORIF, or open-reduction-internal-fixation cases. This particular fracture was a very simple one, so we were going to perform a 'closed reduction.'

The child was put to sleep by the anesthesiologist using a mask induction, monitors were placed, and then an IV was started. After the IV was in, the anesthesiologist intubated the child, and the child was positioned for surgery. With a closed reduction, the surgeon, with the aid of a mini C-arm which is a small X-ray machine, can set the broken bone so that it is in the correct alignment, and then a fiberglass cast is applied to keep the arm in that position until the bone has mended.

To make a cast, a cotton sleeve is placed over the broken arm. Next, soft padding is applied in a circular fashion around the affected arm. Fiberglass cast material is then applied, and comes on a roll. The roll is dipped in a bucket of water, which activates the fiberglass, and then the fiberglass material is wrapped around the child's broken arm. Several rolls are needed to build up the cast to become strong enough. The fiberglass cast material comes in several colors. In just a few minutes, the fiberglass material starts to become hardened.

This particular night, we had a run of children who needed a simple closed reduction fracture repair. It was late at night, and we were all tired. The children all first had to come through the emergency room to be admitted, which takes a minimum of one hour, and sometimes longer. I complained to the rest of the OR crew about how lovely it would be, if we could just drag all our equipment to the emergency room door meeting the children there, and giving the children anesthesia and setting their arms without taking the time for them first to be admitted.

Chapter

21

Mandatory education modules are assigned to each RN throughout the year. The hospital loves to use acronyms in what they think will be a catchy way for the nurse to remember their information. Unfortunately, the poor RN is bombarded during her mandatory education with so many acronyms it is overwhelming! Not to mention that over time, many familiar acronyms are changed!

For example, 'SAVE,' used to be the acronym given for what to do in the event of a fire. 'S' stood for save the patient, 'A' was to activate the alarm, 'V' meant control ventilation, and 'E' stood for extinguishing the fire. Now the acronym for dealing with fires has been changed to 'RACE.' 'R' is for rescue the patient, 'A' stands for activate the alarm, 'C' is for control ventilation, and 'E' still means extinguish the fire. Another example is the acronym FAST, which is supposed to prompt the nurse to look for symptoms of a possible stroke. 'F' was for checking for facial droop, 'A' was to see if the patient could lift both of their arms simultaneously without one arm dropping, 'S' stood for slurred speech, and 'T' was to prompt the nurse that time was of the essence. Now, the acronym has been changed to 'BEFAST,' with the first two letters standing for changes in balance and eyes!

These two examples of acronyms used in training are only the tip of the iceberg when you think of all the multitude of sayings that nurses are supposed to remember! I vaguely remember the acronym 'BEAGLE,' which was to help the nurse remember the components of the time-out given at the beginning of each operation. 'B' was for Beta Blockers and I don't remember what all the other letters stood for. We used to have posters with acronyms plastered all over the walls. I do remember that the 'BEAGLE' poster was next to the wash sinks, where we washed our hands thoroughly before starting our workday in the OR.

Yesterday, a four-year-old girl came in for a strabismus repair. What was unusual was that she suffered from a severe form of Ichthyosis; which presented as her skin was literally sloughing off all of her body! A rotting odor was noted as well. Poor, poor child! The pre-surgery nurses informed me that we could not use any form of tape on the child, which presented a major problem in that the EKG stickers are sticky like tape, as well as we use tape to secure the IV. The mother stated that any tape used would literally pull off the child's skin.

It was not unusual for patients to have an allergy to tape, but usually there was some type of tape that the parent told us we could still use, that did not cause a reaction. Not so for this patient! I wasn't sure how the operation could even go forward, especially without the use of EKG stickers, as well as an IV. We also typically used tape to secure the endotracheal tube to the patient's outer jaw as well! I talked to the anesthesiologist about how the operation could be accomplished. He was a senior anesthesiologist who was very experienced and skilled. He agreed to forgo the EKG leads with stickers, and devised a cloth wrap to hold the endotracheal tube in place.

We placed an IV in the child's foot which we padded with

gauze, and then wrapped the IV site with a cling wrap named Coban. What a horrible disease to have--where all your skin is literally dying and sloughing off constantly. It put all my little health issues in a whole new light as being quite insignificant!

I was working one day as a facilitator, where one of my duties was to bring the patient and their parents from the pre-surgery area where their child had been admitted, down the hall into the holding room next to the OR. There, the parents would talk to the anesthesiologist, the surgeon, and the circulator, before their child's surgery took place. I brought one patient back that only had a father present, and I didn't really notice the father, until I sat down to give him my spiel about what would happen next, where he would go while his child had his operation, etc. As I started to speak, I now noticed how good-looking the father was. He was at least part Hawaiian, and he had zig-zag tattoos all around his muscular arms. I was surprised at myself, to find that I could hardly remember my spiel, as I have given it hundreds of times!

When I went back into the OR to give a report to the circulator of who the next patient was, along with a verbal health history on the patient, I mentioned at the end of my report that the dad was hot. This all took the staff in the OR by surprise, as I am known as being very conservative, (and old). I knew they all would get a kick out of it. Later, as I reentered the OR, they all had teasing comments about me and the hot father. I told them all that I was pleased that I could be their entertainment for the afternoon. It was funny, and the dad was hot! Just because you are old, doesn't mean you are dead!

Today, I was working with Dr. R., the ENT surgeon. When operating on only one side of a body part such as an ear, or one side of the nose, policy requires that the surgeon mark his initials on the correct side. This policy, of course, is to prevent surgeons from working on the wrong body part. Initialing doesn't work too well when the body part is very small, such as an ear or nostril. Dr. R. asked if the surgeon's initials were still the policy for marking the side, and after we confirmed that it was, he quipped with his usual dark wit that instead, he could sign the body part with his autograph--'to all my fans, Charles!' That really struck me as super funny thinking about getting all those words on a tiny body part! Crazy!

As I was leaving work today, I saw Happy, a Korean woman who works here in the hospital as an IV therapist, walking down the hall. She is very short in height, and has to be at least in her late seventies, if not older. She often came to start my IV for procedures when I was being treated for breast cancer seventeen years ago. I remember how fantastic she was--always a smile on her face, and even better; she could always get your IV in on the first try! Seeing her always makes me very pleased that older nurses with that much experience are still on the job!

Working in the children's day surgery has been a hot proposition lately! One element that the OR has to control is room humidity. The reason a low room humidity is needed is to control the growth of bacteria in the surgical suites. The OR has to be shut down if the humidity in the room is over sixty-five percent. This always becomes a problem in the older day surgery building every summer and early fall when the outside temperature can be in the nineties. The air conditioning system, because of its age, cannot keep the temperature low enough without the humidity going up. To combat this problem, the heat is turned up inside the building to about seventy-five degrees, and that drops the humidity. The problem with that, is the staff must not only wear scrubs, but also a cover jacket. The surgeon and person scrubbing must wear a sterile gown, gloves, mask, and eye wear during procedures in a room that was already seventy-five degrees to start with! When we complain to engineering, they tell us that in order to keep the humidity down, the ambient temperature has to stay high! In other words, deal with it!

Yesterday, I scrubbed for Dr. E., a plastic surgeon who has worked part-time as a hospital employee for years. He was unusual, in that he still maintained his independent practice as well. He typically had two full morning blocks scheduled at the hospital every week involving procedures ranging from minor lumps and bumps being removed, to major procedures repairing cleft lips and palates, as well as performing breast reconstructions. These surgeries brought in a lot of revenue for the hospital every year. When his contract came up for renewal with the hospital this year, he was not only not offered a contract, but no word was ever mentioned to him by the hospital administration that they were not renewing, but instead replacing him with another plastic surgeon!

He had just found out that morning before he started his scheduled block of surgeries with us, that his contract was not being renewed. Of course, he was dumbfounded, along with the rest of us! He said he was angry and hurt over the incident, but was very pleasant as usual to work with. He has his own private practice as well, so it is not like he will starve to death. But still! I don't think the hospital administration understands the damage done to the morale of the staff as this news is spread quickly to everyone working in the OR. We all realize that the same disloyalty could be applied to us as well. The plastic surgeon who replaced him does not even come close to bringing in the volume of cases that Dr. E. did. It remains a mystery to me why the hospital let him go.

Dr. G., the wonderful urologist, has decided to give up his independent practice of decades, and to become a hospital employee, as so many other physicians have done. He told me that it is a big relief for him, as he will not have to worry about covering his office and liability costs, as well as his own personal health care premiums. He stated that he has been paying three thousand dollars a month just for his family's health care premiums, and now he will only pay three thousand a year for health care premiums as a hospital employee!

Yesterday, while doing a regular ENT block, the surgeon received a telephone call from the emergency department of our hospital telling him that one of his tonsillectomy patients had just come in with a post-tonsillectomy bleed. The surgeon wanted to work this patient into the block as soon as possible. One of the newer nurses working in the room with us asked me to look up whether the emergency room had started an IV, otherwise she was going to get the supplies together for starting an IV. I responded, "Of course, they started an IV!" It is standard practice when someone comes in with a bleed to start an IV, take some bloodwork like a hematocrit, hang fluid, and even do a type and cross for blood, for the possibility that the patient might need a blood transfusion.

However, when we did receive the patient, she had no IV! I am still dumbfounded over that--what exactly did they do for this patient in the ER? How can they justify the charges the patient will be billed for an emergency room visit, when they didn't even do the bare basics? An anesthesiologist stated sarcastically that now that the patient's wishes are driving health care, perhaps the patient didn't want an IV! When did patients who are not medically trained start to direct their own care? We, as medical caregivers, should be like good parents--we need to do what is best for you, not necessarily what you would prefer.

I was really disappointed in the RN who took care of this patient in the emergency room. Even if the physician forgot or didn't want to start an IV and fluids, the nurse should have insisted that he give her an order for one. If a physician ever refuses to do what the nurse feels is necessary for the patient, the nurse has the option of going over the physician's head and calling the hospital's medical director, who is also a physician. If the medical director agrees with the nurse, the medical director can give the nurse the order she is seeking.

Recently, I had lunch with several nurses that I used to work with on the medical-surgical floor who had recently retired. Surprisingly to me, almost all of them had permanently given up their nursing licenses! Most retired in their early sixties, due to their lack of job satisfaction over their working conditions, and management issues. The sad thing is that most of these nurses could have continued working at least part-time for many more years, providing invaluable experience to newer nurses just beginning to work. A case in point is that a very ill infant with a high fever, which later has a subnormal temperature would appear to an inexperienced pediatric nurse to be getting better. An experienced nurse would recognize that the infant's body is no longer able to combat the infection by maintaining a high temperature, and that the baby is about to go into complete failure, and needs immediate intervention.

It saddened me to think that all of that knowledge and experience that leaves with each retiring nurse, is lost forever, and will never be retrieved. It seems such a shame!

One of my dearest friends teaches students to become registered nurses. Part of her job is administering tests to those students. If a student fails to answer a question correctly, the students are allowed to challenge that question with their instructor; my friend. One question that my friend devised for a test had to do with a post-op patient that seemed unresponsive. Her question asked what would be one of the first things that should be done by the nurse? The answer the teacher was looking for was that the nurse should see if the patient could be aroused; meaning awakened. A student, who had missed that question, told my friend that she had done all the required reading, and had never seen anything about arousing the patient sexually! Of course, my friend meant that the nurse should see if the patient could be aroused by calling his name and shaking him gently. We laughed and laughed, over the fact that young people no longer think of the word arousal, without it having a sexual connotation.

We recently had two siblings as patients in the children's day surgery center. One was a three-year-old boy who was calling all of the staff a #!*. (Use your imagination!) We finished his operation, and took him back to the recovery room. Next up was his seven-year-old sister, who was even worse, and was loaded with attitude to boot. As she sat upright in her hospital stretcher in the holding room, I asked her politely if I could look at her name band on her wrist, which I am required to do. Most older children her age are usually very cooperative. Not her! She put her arm with the name band behind her back, and told me I wouldn't be seeing her name band until she saw her cousin, who apparently was someone she thought very highly of. She went on with her vocal tirade, proving to me that I was going to need help getting her safely back to the OR suite. Unlike her children, the mother seemed very polite and nice, as I interviewed her before both of her children's operations. She appeared to be very embarrassed at her children's behavior, and now stood mutely by as her daughter refused to cooperate with me.

I went back and got one of my co-workers to come to my aid. As we came back into the holding room, the girl's mother, who was mortified at her daughter's behavior, slipped out of the room, and went to wait in the surgical waiting area.

With the two of us alone with the disobedient child, I explained to the girl that we could go back to the OR one of two ways. We could roll back nice and easy with her co-operating; or we could both hang onto her as we went back. She said that she wanted to go back the nice way, although I could tell she was getting ready to vault over the stretcher's safety rails, and make a break for freedom. I advised my co-worker of my suspicions, so my co-worker, who was completely unfamiliar with this little girl, grasped ahold of the girl's arm, keeping her safely on the stretcher. The girl quickly responded with, "You get your fat fingers off of my arm!" If only I had had a camera to take a picture of my co-worker's face! Her eyes were wide with astonishment! As we rolled past the secretary, his face too, became one of amazement, as he heard the girl abusing us verbally. Later, after the operation was completed, we rolled back to the recovery room with our patient. The recovery room nurses informed us that the three-year-old boy who was still in recovery, was calling all of them a #!*. (use your imagination!)

Even though I informed the recovery room nurse that this girl was a sibling to the three-year-old boy, she still hadn't quite grasped that information. As I was getting ready to leave the recovery room, the nurse stopped me and said, "Are these two children siblings?" "Yes," I said. "She is the sister of the three-year-old boy and is like him, only three times worse." The nurse looked incredulous as she took in this information.

After returning to the OR, and after starting another case, all of us in the OR were wondering what diatribes our seven-year-old girl was dishing out to the recovery nurses. Since we had two circulators in our case, I volunteered to go down the hall to the recovery room to find out what was happening there. Usually, patients are kept in recovery for at least half-an-hour, so that the nurse can make sure the patient's pain is controlled, and that they look somewhat presentable to the parents. As I walked into the recovery room, I was surprised to see that the girl was not in there, even though we had brought her there only fifteen minutes earlier! According to the recovery room nurse, as soon as the girl awoke, and started dishing out her verbal abuse with attitude, they had shipped her out to her mother, so that she could deal with her out there. (along with the poor nurses who now had the duty of caring for her.)

One Valentine's day, I had a handsome, two-year-old boy for one of my patients. He was there to have a minor elective surgery. He was a little loopy from his preoperative sedative, but was still sitting upright in his crib as we rolled down the long hall to the operating room with his mother by his side. When we came to the point where we had to say goodbye to his mother, the boy puckered up to give his mom a kiss. She bent down, he kissed her, then turned to me with puckered lips. I also bent down, and he gave me a nice kiss on my cheek. How sweet is that? I think that is the first time I have ever had a patient give me a kiss, and it tickled me all day to think of it...........who says there isn't love on Valentine's Day?

As health care continues to evolve, we as a society, will have to decide how to spend our health care dollars. Expensive diagnostic tests and treatments will continue to be developed. Who will be brave enough to ask the difficult ethical questions? If we have limited resources, who will get those health dollars? What politician will be brave enough to oppose lobbyists, and bring up the topic of limiting the liability of health care workers in order to keep premium costs down? As we all know in this society, businesses are all trying to make money for their shareholders, or themselves. As individuals, we can't be able to sue our health care providers for millions of dollars for damages, and yet have low health care premiums. The choice is either one, or the other.

What senator or congressperson would be brave enough to bring up the topic of limiting the profits made by the pharmaceutical companies or better yet, having our government produce some drugs and vaccines here in the United States for no profit? Most of the general public do not realize that there are frequent shortages of inexpensive drugs commonly used in this country by anesthesiologists and surgeons on a daily basis.

As I write this piece, there is a shortage of medications used as intradermal locals containing epinephrine used to numb surgical areas, and to reduce bleeding. I can only think that these drugs don't make a huge profit for the pharmaceutical companies, therefore their manufacture is not a high priority. One anesthesiologist in the hospital I work at, told me that she felt like she was having to give care in a third world country, because of the lack of common drugs that had become unavailable to her, that she would normally use on a daily basis!

When will we learn to spend our resources on preventive health care, instead of on hospitalizations and emergency room visits, that affect the cost of everyone's health insurance premiums? We spend millions in this country, if not billions, on the hospitalization, and ongoing therapies for premature infants, whose early birth are many times a direct result of their mothers never having received prenatal care because of their lack of health care insurance.

We could spend our health care dollars more wisely. In other countries, local community clinics serve the everyday needs of their people more inexpensively. The elderly can go to a local clinic, have their blood pressure monitored, discuss the medications they are taking, and make any adjustments necessary. In our country, the elderly who are usually on several medications that can easily affect their body's delicate equilibrium, often end up in the emergency room because they have forgotten how to take their medication correctly, and who are then hospitalized until they are stabilized. Having a local clinic that could serve them for low or no cost, would save health care dollars by preventing, or reducing their hospitalizations.

A local clinic staffed by a nurse practitioner or physician's assistant would be more than capable of taking care of most people's health issues for the lowest cost. If one of their patient's has a more serious problem, the nurse practitioner or physician's assistant could refer the patient on to see the necessary physician needed.

Emergency rooms really should be for emergencies only, not used as local community clinics as they are now, especially for the millions of citizens that are uninsured.

Vaccines should be readily available at the local level for all of our citizens to receive. Providing free vaccines along with education regarding health issues, would be a fabulous use of our health care dollars. As the old saying goes, an ounce of prevention is worth a pound of cure. Many of our vaccines are not produced in our country. Our country should not rely on other countries to produce vaccines that we need for our citizens. Let's spend our health care dollars intelligently.

Making working conditions less stressful for hospital nurses would increase the nurse's longevity in the workplace. There has been a nursing shortage in this country for several years. A finite number of nurses graduate every year due to the limited number of nursing school openings. I personally know of several people who decided that they wanted to become a registered nurse, and applied for nursing school. After being accepted by the school, they took one of the very limited nursing school slots and graduated, only to end up working for a very short time, or never working, before quitting nursing altogether! With a nursing shortage, everything should be done to retain working nurses. In the hospital setting, certified nursing assistants or other less expensive help could be hired to work with the registered nurses. This would alleviate the workload for the registered nurse, freeing her up to do the more difficult tasks that she was trained to perform.

Older nurses, with their invaluable knowledge after years of experience working, should be encouraged to stay in the workforce. To keep older nurses in the workforce, hospitals could make special allowances, such as eliminating the requirement for older nurses having to take call. Older nurses could also be used as special resource nurses, where they are not required to do difficult physical tasks such as the heavy lifting of patients, but instead, could be utilized to give younger, less-experienced nurses advice in various situations involving patients.

We, as individuals, can do our part in keeping health care costs down. Preventative care is essential. We can make sure that we, and our family members, receive our vaccinations, which prevent many different diseases. We should strive to maintain a healthy lifestyle, which would include eating healthily, exercising, not smoking, as well as limiting any alcohol consumption. Having regular screening exams for various types of cancer are important. We should be sure and practice good oral hygiene, along with having regular dental visits. Any measure we can take to prevent disease, and keep healthy, should be our goal.

In the end, it is up to us as a nation to decide how to spend our health dollars. Besides managing our own health, our only other power is in letting our representatives in Congress and the Senate know how we feel.

We can also tell our nurses and physicians that care for us how much we appreciate their help.

S.F. Johnson lives in the Pacific Northwest, along with her sweet husband of many decades. She is the proud mother of four children, and the grandmother of thirteen.

She works part-time as a pediatric nurse in a local children's hospital. She enjoys gardening, reading, watching movies, sewing, and painting. She is the author of several books.

Made in the USA
Las Vegas, NV
14 February 2021

17804729R00134